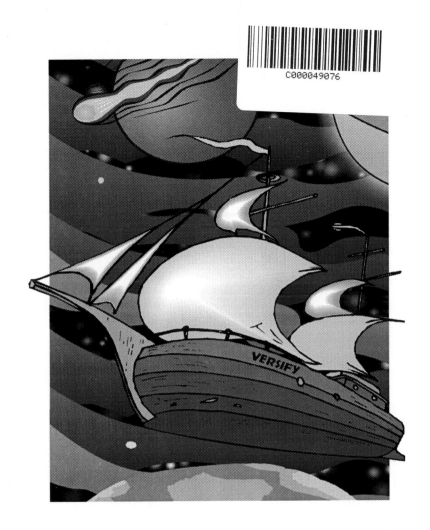

POETIC VOYAGES
SITTINGBOURNE

Edited by Steve Twelvetree

First published in Great Britain in 2001 by
YOUNG WRITERS
Remus House,
Coltsfoot Drive,
Peterborough, PE2 9JX
Telephone (01733) 890066

HB ISBN 0 75433 126 1
SB ISBN 0 75433 127 X

FOREWORD

Young Writers was established in 1991 with the aim to promote creative writing in children, to make reading and writing poetry fun.

This year once again, proved to be a tremendous success with over 88,000 entries received nationwide.

The Poetic Voyages competition has shown us the high standard of work and effort that children are capable of today. It is a reflection of the teaching skills in schools, the enthusiasm and creativity they have injected into their pupils shines clearly within this anthology.

The task of selecting poems was therefore a difficult one but nevertheless, an enjoyable experience. We hope you are as pleased with the final selection in *Poetic Voyages Sittingbourne* as we are.

CONTENTS

Minterne County Junior School

Rebecca Reed	67
Jake Brissenden	68
Shane Priston	68
Lewis Tumber	68
George Luther	69
Alice Hughes	69
Glen Thomson	69
Aimee Patrick	70
Zoë Blogg	70
Stephen Jacobs	71
Adam Green	71
Anthony West	72
Samantha Oliver	72
Robert Mills	72
Ian Kingsman	73
Georgina Winney	73
Fiona Cordes	73
Johnathon Ralph	74
Kirstie Macmaster	74
Alice Bonney	75
Chloe Fosbraey	75
Arron O'Grady	76
Christian Collins	76
Cassie Glenn	77
Oliver Halls	77
Charlie Kavanagh	78
Emily Blackwell	78
Amy Adlington	78
Kieran Taylor	79
Lloyd Waghorn	79
Lucy Todd	80
Matthew Knell	80
James Smith	81
James Watson	81
Nathan Temple	82
Kingsley Currie	82
Harriet Burns	83

Hayley Beard	83
Anand Sahota	84
Emily Crutchley	85
Joseph Bowerman	85
Peter Easton	86
Peter Terry	86
Jordan Tydeman	87
Declan Douglas	88
Christopher Wilson	88
Andrew Kitney	89
Lucy Gallagher	89
Kirsty Rogers	90
Thomas Sales	90
Laura Wood	91
Megan Bartlet	91
Stephanie Hyams	92
Claire Streatfield	92
Hollie Vallis	93
Rebecca Simmons	93
Scott Barney	94
Alex Betts	94
Sarah Harwood	95
Jamie Ferris	95
Jade Seamer	96
Luke Tumber	97
Victoria Bowerman	98
Victoria Goodger	99
Liam Golchehreh	99
Anthony Aldridge	100
Jordan Buckner	100
Sam Blackwell	101
Alice Evans	102

South Avenue Junior School

Matthew Jewiss	102
Charlotte Tobin	103
Luke Edwards	103
Gareth Messenger	104

The Poems

FIREWORKS

Fireworks whistling
Crackling in the sky
Fireworks banging
Way up high.

Fireworks green
Yellow and white
Fireworks gold
And silver bright.

Fireworks in the garden
Are lovely to see
Firework displays
You watch with great glee.

Firework fountain
Shower the ground
Firework Catherine wheel
Spinning round and round.

Firework rocket
Shooting to the sky
Firework sparklers
Shine in your eye.

Louise Apps (10)
Barrow Grove Junior School

JANUARY

January bleak, January cold
January icy, January bold
January nippy, January frozen
Winter snow cold as ice.

Joshua Coulter (10)
Barrow Grove Junior School

I'M BORED

I'm bored, I don't know what to do
Christmas is over
And everyone just ignores me.

I'm bored, I don't know what to do
The weather is boring
I can't play outside.

I'm bored, I don't know what to do
My toys are all broken
So now I can't play.

I'm excited, I do know what to do
The summer is here
I'm going to get my shoes on
And go outside to play.

Christopher Dodsworth (10)
Barrow Grove Junior School

JANUARY

January is snowy,
January is cold,
January is frosty,
January is bare,
January is icy,
But I don't really care.

I still play with my friends,
We have lots of fun,
Although it is icy we can still see the sun.

Abbey Titchner (9)
Barrow Grove Junior School

THE SNOW KING

Christmas has gone and it's not so much fun
Me and my friends are feeling all glum!
Everything's white, it really looks dull
And near my house is a seagull!

I wrap up warm because it's so chilly
When we're in the snow my brother goes silly!
We've got nothing to do, it's just a bore
But you wouldn't believe what I just saw!

Right in my garden was the Snow King
He saw we were sad so his wand made a fling!
Now thanks to him it's sunny, not boring at all
We're having some fun at playing football!

Adam Visser (10)
Barrow Grove Junior School

THE AUTUMN GARDEN

Leaves falling from the trees.
Brown and crunchy, so crunchy.
They make a crackly sound.
Most of the leaves are falling
on the ground.
The squirrel is coming out of its hole
and looking out.
It is very cold and windy and the
conkers are falling off
and the squirrel is looking out to see
the leaves falling on the ground.

Aaron Crosswell (9)
Barrow Grove Junior School

I'M BORED

I'm bored, there's nothing to do
It's cold, I hate winter
I have to go to school

At least I have friends to play with
In the cold the whistle has gone
We go in the warm and do work.

David Weston (9)
Barrow Grove Junior School

JANUARY

Christmas has gone,
January has started,
January cold, tired, but I'm warm-hearted
January, think . . . new year's resolutions
No more cakes, biscuits,
But solutions to my problems.

Amber Adgie (10)
Barrow Grove Junior School

ETHAN

A human being
A walking object with legs
And a big show off
He likes to wear rings to school
He wants to be Ben Wood's friend.

Sabad Momin (11)
Barrow Grove Junior School

JANUARY

J anuary is a time of coldness
A ll children play outside less
N obody likes this time of year
U nlike summer that brings us cheer
A n alleyway of breeziness
R eally, really freeziness
Y eah, it's really sneeziness.

Danielle Thomson (10)
Barrow Grove Junior School

JANUARY

Oh boy, it's January and cold.
I can feel frost nipping my nose.
I wish I could have some hot chocolate.
Sometimes I like January because
we can build snowmen if it snows.

Chloe Wrigley (9)
Barrow Grove Junior School

COLD

C old, chilly snow covers
O ver the wet,
L onely fields for
D ays and days and days.

Stephen Sissons (9)
Barrow Grove Junior School

A JOURNEY THROUGH THE YEAR

Bitter biting January
Freezing cold February
Nose-twitching March
Shower falling April
Flower exploding May
Sunbathing June
Grass growing July
Lazy old August
Apple reddening September
Leaves falling October
Bonfireing November
Excited December.

Sam Bacon (10)
Barrow Grove Junior School

OUTSIDE

Outside of my room
It's very cold
I walk down the stairs,
I put on my gloves and walk outside,
I look around there's a whole new world
The leaves are on the ground
Bare branches on the trees
The wind is getting colder
The trees are swaying to and fro
The trees are boogying on blowy days.

Rachael Bidgood (10)
Barrow Grove Junior School

OUTSIDE

Outside the leaves
  are falling off the trees
Outside the breeze
  is going at an easy ease
Outside it's cold
  the weather stands bold
Outside my house
  I stand and pounce
Outside I ride
  through the leaves at the
  foot of the trees.

Louise Foreman (10)
Barrow Grove Junior School

THE CAT

Alley prowler
Night howler

Mouse stalker
Smooth walker

Tail twitching
Stare bewitching

Warmth lover
Leg cover.

Christabel McCooey (11)
Barrow Grove Junior School

JANUARY DAYS

It's cold, it's frosty, it's chilly
　　　in January
It's icy, it's lifeless, it's windy
　　　in January
It's grey, it's cloudy, it's white
　　　in January
It's black, it's dark, it's grim
　　　in January

Nathan Bond (9)
Barrow Grove Junior School

INSIDE OUT

Mum, Mum inside out my jumper is.
Dad, Dad inside out my T-shirt is.
Sister, Sister inside out my trousers are.
Pants, socks inside out.
But now, it's out on a January day
All wrapped up warm, ready to play
Now I'm outside, ready to play,
And now I'm so cold even to say . . .

Harrison Bennett (10)
Barrow Grove Junior School

JANUARY

January is here now
Cold and crispy, damp
My hands always get cold
I am going on camp.

I slip on the icy puddle
Fall down with a crash!
The snow running down my face
I trip on a rock with a bash!

Danielle Leppenwell (10)
Barrow Grove Junior School

FRIENDS MOVED

Outside in the snow with no one to play with
And it's a cold, cold night,
And the snowflakes are falling from the sky.
No friends - all gone and moved.

It's summer now, new friends have come.
It's warm and the sunshine is coming from the sky.
Butterflies fly way up high.

Jade Hollands (10)
Barrow Grove Junior School

GOING TO SCHOOL

It was January and it was nearly time to go to school
I was bored and very cold,
It would be worse if you were bald
But I had friends so it's all right.
I walked to school and Adam gave me a fright
I played at school and came out tall.
I woke up in the morning,
Fell out of bed and I hurt my poor old head.

William Hillman (9)
Barrow Grove Junior School

JANUARY NIGHTS

January is a cold time, jumpers, frost, snowball fights.
January is not my favourite month, bitter cold, black, blue, white.
January is frightening, chilly and dull.
Bored and bleak I sit here staring out of the window at the rain.
The snow, the ice and the inky skies looking wise.
I'm cold staring at my bed,
It's warm and cosy; heat steaming from my hot water bottle.
It's no good, I have to get into the lovely warm sheets.

Sheena Fathers (9)
Barrow Grove Junior School

SNOW

S   o chilly, so icy
N   obody knows how the chill gets in.
      Biting at our frozen bodies.
O   h, the snow makes me shiver, it's so
W   hite and crisp. When it snows it makes
      me feel all chilly inside.

Sarah Taylor (8)
Barrow Grove Junior School

COLD

C   old people
O   utside in the winter,
L   ooking chilled - as cold as ice.
D   ancing all around the bleak, cutting snow.

Adi Lari (8)
Barrow Grove Junior School

WINTER

W inter snow falls to the ground.
I cicles hang from the roof.
N ice and warm in my cosy bed.
T ea, steaming hot in my mug.
E ating cheese on toast.
R eading my favourite book
    by the warm, glowing fire.

Andrew Gilbert (8)
Barrow Grove Junior School

WINTER

W hite snow falling heavily from the grey sky
I like to build a snowman
N ice and high
T rees sway happily in the icy wind
E veryone enjoys playing their games
R unning round and round and round.

Tara Norris (8)
Barrow Grove Junior School

WHITE

White snow falling steadily from the pale grey sky
I like to build a snowman nice and high
Trees swaying gently in the icy wind
Everyone enjoying playing the games,
Running round and round.

Ross Jones (9)
Barrow Grove Junior School

COLD

C old, white snow lays on the ground,
   covering all the food for the birds.
O nly nooks and crannies welcome the
   birds to feast.
L ooking out at the soft, crunchy snow
   that is falling,
D elivering a cold, dark, gloomy sky
   within the bleak winter.

Michael Button (9)
Barrow Grove Junior School

FLOWERS

Flowers are big
Flowers are small
Flowers are tiny
Flowers are bright
Flowers are bold
Flowers are pretty
In shops they are sold.

Emily Killick (9)
Barrow Grove Junior School

COLD

C old snow falling from the bleak grey sky. Lots
O f happy children making snowmen and playing snowballs
L aughing with each other. I wish it was snowing every
D ay. I enjoy the long, snowy days.

Robert Meaney (8)
Barrow Grove Junior School

A LION

A lion, a lion
The king of the jungle
The big purry cat
With razor-sharp teeth and claws
With a furry coat
Its magnificent leap
Its mighty roar
The king of the jungle lives on.

Nazia Uddin (10)
Barrow Grove Junior School

COLD

C old winter nights,
O ver the hills the wind is whistling
    through the trees.
L iving in a cottage,
    snuggling up in bed,
D ark and spooky without candlelight.

Emma Francis (9)
Barrow Grove Junior School

A CAT

A tabby walking
Purring while being let out
Watching quietly
Licking herself with her tongue
Lazily asleep on bed.

Emma Ansley (10)
Barrow Grove Junior School

Autumn Days

Autumn days, the leaves will fall,
Winter will soon come to call.
Leaves are all brown in colour;
I don't think they could be much duller.
They're also yellow and red I agree,
But that is still not good enough for me.
Autumn days are those I hate,
It's a good job autumn is so late.

Tom Godkin (11)
Barrow Grove Junior School

Rat

Big eater
Treat lover
Fast runner
Long tail
Black headed
White bodied.

Odette Carrier (11)
Barrow Grove Junior School

Tiger

Flesh eater
Animal killer
Pouncing tiger
Bone licker.

Kirsty Male (10)
Barrow Grove Junior School

LEAVES

Leaves
Rustling leaves
Falling, rustling leaves
Crunching, falling, rustling leaves
Brown, crunching, falling, rustling leaves
Red, brown, crunching, falling, rustling leaves
Brown, crunching, falling, rustling leaves
Crunching, falling, rustling leaves
Falling, rustling leaves
Rustling leaves
Leaves.

Alex Tooke (10)
Barrow Grove Junior School

ALONE LITTLE BOY

Alone on his own
Sitting like a stuffed lemon
Now he's getting bored
He's now starting to doze off
'Goodnight you boring old world.'

Daniel Friend (11)
Barrow Grove Junior School

HAIKU

A brilliant game!
A superb football player
Is David Beckham.

Michael Yates (10)
Barrow Grove Junior School

MY BROTHER LOVES BANANAS

When my brother's got bananas
he is a banana too
he makes them into pirates
or the captain's crew.

When my brother's got bananas
he puts them in his shoes
or makes them into people
on a Caribbean cruise.

When my brother's got bananas
he sticks them up his nose
he slides them on his fingers
even on his toes.

My brother loves bananas
they give him such fun
but what you've got to remember
is my brother's only one.

Charlotte Peters (9)
Barrow Grove Junior School

WOLF

Midnight dancer,
Moonlight howler,
Squirrel killer,
Full moon lover,
Animal teaser,
Gut squeezer.

Answer: Wolf

Jack Holmes (11)
Barrow Grove Junior School

INSIDE THE ELEMENTS

Inside the fire a cindering heat
Inside the cindering heat a blazing light
Inside the blazing light a sparkling ruby
Inside the sparkling ruby a sun
Inside the sun flames of rage
Inside the flames of rage is ash
Inside the ash was fire

Inside the water a chilling cold
Inside the chilling cold a shimmering mirror
Inside the shimmering mirror a stream of diamonds
Inside the stream of diamonds a shattering wetness
Inside the shattering wetness is dried ground

Inside the ground is a damp warmth
Inside the damp warmth is moisture
Inside the moisture a burst of light
Inside the burst of light dirty rain falls
Inside the rain is chocolate-like lakes
Inside the chocolate-like lakes was ground.

Tyler Attwood (10)
Barrow Grove Junior School

FESTIVE DAYS

Cheerful, full of joy
Gleeful, jolly and proud

Blissful and blessed
Joyful and over the moon
Thrilled and ecstatic.

Michael Bean (10)
Barrow Grove Junior School

SOMETHING FISHY

I knew an old woman
but something was wrong
her favourite pet was a goldfish
and I already knew
that there was *something fishy*.

She had a long coat
you couldn't see any part of her body
she said she liked to swim
and I already knew
that there was *something fishy*

She was so silent
her back was always wet
and the cats were always around her
and I already knew
that there was *something fishy*.

I decided to spy on her that night
I followed her to the lake
she released the coat and guess what I saw?
Yes, *something fishy*.

She was a goldfish
a tank was over her head
she took off the tank and took her pet
yes, *something fishy*.

She jumped into the lake
and all the cats ran there
she was gone, never seen again
Yes, so fishy, something fishy
Is it a myth, legend or fable?
No *something fishy*.

Alise Carstens (10)
Barrow Grove Junior School

ANGRY AND SAD

Angry
When I am angry
I get extremely mental,
I'm red in the face,
I hit out and scream a lot,
That's me when I am angry.

> *Sad*
> When I'm very sad
> I try to cry quite a bit
> To get attention,
> But it hardly ever works,
> That's me when I am quite sad.

Aaron Lamb (10)
Barrow Grove Junior School

TREES

The trees are swaying
The squirrels are climbing the trees
The leaves are falling
The leaves are red, orange and yellow on the trees
Chestnuts are falling
Chestnuts are on the ground
Hard shiny conkers are falling onto soft green grass
Conker shells are spiky
People gathering conkers and smashing their shells
The wind is blowing
The squirrels are running past me.

Russell Kent (9)
Barrow Grove Junior School

A WINTER NIGHT

Street lamps shine on the ground
Children sleep snug and sound
Little animals creep around

Big animals swoop down
Flashing lights in the town
Owls' eyes big and brown
Teenagers act like big clowns.

Good morning

Stevee Butt (9)
Barrow Grove Junior School

MY TRIP TO THE SEASIDE

Sand, sand everywhere,
Sand in your shoes
Sand in your hair
And sand in your swimming costume,
Sand in your pants
Sand in your ears
Sand in-between your toes,
It may tickle when you go to bed
I had sand all over my pillow.

Louise Ralph (8)
Barrow Grove Junior School

MY TEACHER

Miss Roberts is a really nice teacher
She is always happy
She is sometimes funny
I like my teacher very much.

She is kind and helpful
But sometimes she shouts
I don't like it when she shouts
But I still like my teacher.

Katie Dodsworth (8)
Barrow Grove Junior School

AUTUMN

I heard the children scraping their feet
    in the leaves on the ground,
I smelt the smoke of all the bonfires,
I heard the crackling of the fires blasting up,
I smelt the lovely apple pies
    baking in the oven,
I heard the wind blowing strongly on the trees,
When I smell and hear these things I know
    that autumn is here.

Avril Jarrett (10)
Barrow Grove Junior School

A TRIP TO THE BEACH

When I go to the beach it's so much fun,
Laughing and paddling with everyone.
We build sandcastles and dig up my dad,
While my mum is lying and bathing in the golden sand.

I have ice-cream with my fish and chips,
While my mum and dad have loads of bread sticks.
We go crab hunting and have a laugh,
While my mum keeps saying, 'You lot are daft.'

Jessica Bransfield (8)
Barrow Grove Junior School

THE HAIRY SCARY SPIDER

The hairy scary spider
came down from his web
and landed straight in my bed.
I screamed and shouted for my mum,
when she got there the spider had run.
'What's the matter?' she said,
as she put me back in my bed.
'There was a hairy scary spider!'

Jessica Butler (7)
Barrow Grove Junior School

SLOTH

Look up in the sky at the tree,
What in the world
Is that you see?
A little sloth
As sweet as can be
Munching on leaves
Very slowly indeed!

Emma Leadbetter (10)
Barrow Grove Junior School

FROST

F   rosty, cold mornings when the grass is crunchy.
R   eally freezing cold snowflakes are falling silently
O   n the tip of your nose,
S   liding gently down your frozen chin.
T   all trees are getting covered with crunchy, white,
     icy cold frost.

Amber Horsford (9)
Barrow Grove Junior School

SNOWMAN

S nowman tucked up in the hard
N estling snow.
O ld buttons and mangy carrots forming
part of his uniform
W hile children dab him with their
warm insulated
M ittens,
A nd caressing him with tender love
N ight and day.

Rianne Dighton (9)
Barrow Grove Junior School

DEAR TOOTH FAIRY

My name is Samantha
And here is the truth
I was eating a sweet
When I swallowed my tooth
My smile is now gappy
Which makes me unhappy
So please leave a penny or two.

Avril Simpson (9)
Barrow Grove Junior School

COLD

C old snow falls slowly and steadily
O ver the frozen floor. You get a thick
L ayer of blanketed snow. Snowmen -
D o feel the freezing cold - don't they?

Jack Chambers (8)
Barrow Grove Junior School

WINTER

W indy winter, what a shame,
I think the earth must be cold with
  dashing snow breathing through it.
N o soil, it's disappeared under a
  blanket of cracking ice.
T rees are shivering, getting colder like
E xposed Arctic waters. Picking ice,
  ouch! That's cold. My ears are
R ed with painful, cold and it is
  getting colder and colder.

Ross Boswell (9)
Barrow Grove Junior School

WHITE

W hite is in winter.
H as snow just got white in it?
I would like to know why snow is white.
T he ground is green, the snow is white.
E very single snowflake is white,
  glistening and pure.

Jamie Burgess (8)
Barrow Grove Junior School

TRAMPOLINING

Up, down, up, down, up,
Front drop, seat drop, a full twist
Landing so soundly.

Helen Baldock (10)
Barrow Grove Junior School

MY TEACHER

Loves to shout
Don't let you out
Spelling lover
Break time hater
Home time keeper
Homework giver

But we still like her.

Emily Kent (11) & Clare Forster (10)
Barrow Grove Junior School

RAIN

First rain is spitting,
then it starts to pour.
Mats are floating
as it spreads across the floor.

Roads turn into rivers,
buses turn into boats.
All the people on board are a-shiver.
thanks for anything that floats.

Water is rising,
when is it going to stop?
Only a few months ago
we did not have a drop.

Emily Gent (11)
Bobbing Village CP School

SADNESS

Here I sit at Bobbing School
I am now the class fool.
All I want is some friends that won't
drive me round the bend.
When I was new it wasn't so bad,
but now I am known
I am real sad.
All my life I thought
it was getting nice
but there it goes.
If I weren't smart I'd be liked,
I know it happens out of spite.
Oh well, I'm going down and
I'll sink.
It's such a shame I'm who I am,
if I was silly and real bad
maybe I wouldn't be so sad.
There's no way of changing who I am
which is such a shame.

Who I am, I just don't know,
all I know is
there's no place for me here.
I know all people think I am mad,
but what is so bad.
If I had friends maybe it wouldn't drive me
round the bend.

Craig Miners (10)
Bobbing Village CP School

SNOW

Snow falling from the sky,
everyone's waving goodbye as the holidays start.
Everyone's freezing cold,
as they wait for that man who's big and bold,
and everyone's so, so cold,
as the . . .

Snow's falling from the sky,
slowly falling down to the ground,
as a child sees that man who's big and round.
Soon he leaves to give the gifts out,
he walks through the soft, white, slippery snow.

Lois Hooper (11)
Bobbing Village CP School

UNTITLED

We take the micky
out of Nicky,
because he is mean
just like his jeans.
We have a cat
but Nicky calls it a bat.
We have a mum
but he cuts her thumbs.
We have a dog
but Nicky flushed his head
down the bog.
He has left us now!

Victoria Ewen (11)
Bobbing Village CP School

CHRISTMAS

Christmas is happy,
Just for me.
Christmas is flappy,
And also clappy.

The presents are joyful.
When you open them,
You feel as beautiful as can be.

James Stowe (10)
Bobbing Village CP School

THE ACROBAT BIRD

One day at the zoo
I heard a bird coo and coo.
This bird caught my eye
I saw him try and try.
He lifted a weight first,
Second, he did the splits,
He did the handstand third
And that's the tale of the acrobat bird.

Farren Tyler Budden (10)
Bobbing Village CP School

CHIPS THE HAMSTER

She wakes up,
Runs around,
Pitter-patter
On the ground!

Up through the tube,
Down to her nest,
Nibbles some food,
Must have a rest!

Katy Fosbraey (9)
Grove Park CP School

THE WITCH'S SPELL

Bubble, bubble joy and tumble,
Fire burn and cauldron bubble,

Sticky buns and chocolate cakes,
In the cauldron boil and bake,
Add a slice of blueberry pie,
Or maybe some coloured dye,
Burger and chips with mushy peas,
Add a good dollop of plain cheese,
Liver and chips with mushy peas,
Add a bowl of my favourite greens.

Bubble, bubble joy and tumble,
Fire burn and cauldron bubble.

Chocolate buns and strawberry cakes,
In the cauldron boil and bake,
Add a slice of apple pie,
Or maybe some coloured dye.

Bubble, bubble joy and tumble,
Fire burn and cauldron bubble,

Ham and mushrooms,
In the cauldron boil and bake.

Bubble, bubble joy and tumble,
Fire burn and cauldron bubble.

Lauren Cheeseman (9)
Grove Park CP School

SCHOOL

In my school:-
The whiteboard is as plain as snow
Lights as bright as the sun
Tables as still as ice
The teachers as nice as pie.

My school is held together by:-
Friends as nice as family
Bricks as hard as graphite
Fire extinguisher which is a lifesaver
        better than a fire brigade
The cables as wiry as a pattern that twists.

In my school I treasure:-
The playground, the most precious thing on Earth
The teachers as nice as my family
The globe as round as a basketball
The heaters as warm as the middle of the sun.

Leonie Bassett (9)
Grove Park CP School

MY PET RABBIT - FLOPSY

I'd rather have a rabbit,
Than a dog or cat.
I'd rather have a rabbit,
Than a gerbil or a rat.

I love my pet rabbit,
His name is Flopsy B.
I love my pet rabbit,
Although he is naughty.

Once he chewed through the wire,
On our Christmas tree.
My mum and dad told him off,
And said you bad rabbit Flopsy.

I'd rather have a rabbit,
Than a dog or a cat.
I'd rather have a rabbit,
Than a gerbil or a rat.

Rebecca Rayner (8)
Grove Park CP School

MY SCHOOL SIMILIES POEM

In my school I have;
Books like soldiers, standing to attention,
Heaters as warm as a summer's midday,
An overhead projector like a machine from outer space,
And teachers like a fountain of wisdom.

My school is held together by;
Friendship as tight as cuddling a teddy bear,
Children being as good as gold,
Headmaster like the captain of a ship,
And assemblies like a service in a church.

In my school I treasure;
Memories like a picture stuck in your mind,
Library as quiet as a mouse,
Choir singing as sweetly as the mid-summer's dew,
And learning as great as can be.

Emma-Rose Ellis (10)
Grove Park CP School

SWEET TOOTH

Yummy yummy sweets are nice,
chocolate from the fridge as cold as ice.

Yum yum bubblegum, blowing like a bubble,
sticky on my shirt and clothes, oh boy I'll be in trouble.

Liquorice laces sugary and sweet,
Three in my mouth so hard to eat.

Crispy crunchy Smarties, colourful and bright,
sneaking in my bedroom to eat them all at night.

Sticky buns and doughnuts topped with fluffy cream,
I'd love to eat them all day long, this is my favourite dream.

Alexander Wharfe (9)
Grove Park CP School

SMILING

When you smile at someone
Who looks really blue
They will start to be happy
And they will smile too.
And when they start to smile
They will pass it on
To someone who looks gloomy
And really feels quite wrong.
Then the whole world will smile
With happiness and joy
And you will find a smile
In every girl and boy.

Ellis Coomber (8)
Grove Park CP School

MacRatty's Rat Rap

I can swim and I can ski,
And I can even cook for my family.
Because I'm MacRatty and MacRatty's me.
You can try but you can't catch me.
Yes, I'm MacRatty and MacRatty's me,
And I'm a rat with ability.

I can read and I can draw,
And I can count to forty-four.
Because I'm MacRatty and MacRatty's me.
You can try but you can't catch me.
Yes, I'm MacRatty and MacRatty's me
And I'm a rat with ability.

Sunjit Atwal (7)
Grove Park CP School

My Imaginary Friend

My imaginary friend follows me about,
Everywhere!
In my house and at my school,
Everywhere!
My imaginary friend is always next to me,
Everywhere!
And she always goes *everywhere* I go.

Stephanie Higgins (8)
Grove Park CP School

IN MY SCHOOL

In my school I have;
Books, which stand like soldiers in a row,
Paper, which is as white as snow,
Dictionaries, which are like spelling teachers,
Globes, which are as round as beachballs.

My school is held together by;
Friendship, which is as important as learning,
Good behaviour, which is as rare as elephants,
Work, which is as dull as staring into space,
Homework, which is like a really annoying sister.

In my school I treasure;
Plants, which are green as grass,
Teachers, which are as gentle as a feather,
Computers, which are like a mechanical teacher,
Students, which are bright as fluorescent pens.

Robyn Pointer (9)
Grove Park CP School

IN MY SCHOOL I HAVE . . .

In my school I have;
Teachers as gentle as butterflies
And a head teacher as nice as pie
Tables as still as day
Little infants like gnomes

My school is held together by;
Friends as funny as clowns
People as quick as light
Boys as quick as mice
Helpers like rabbits that are nice

In my school I treasure;
Grass as green as a lizard
People as quick as blizzards
A drinking fountain as cold as ice
School dinners as nice as rice.

Chloe Dakin (9)
Grove Park CP School

SIMILE

In my school I have;

A playground as fun as Disneyland,
Dictionary, as thick as a brick,
A fire bell, as red as blood,
Pencil case as noisy as metal.

My school is held up by;

Friendship as pleasant as cake,
Jumpers as blue as the sea,
School as sturdy as giant muscles,
Cheeks as red as roses.

I treasure in my school;

Globes as round as a 3-D sphere
Fire bell as red as blood
Pencil pots as new as gold
Calculators as helpful as a teacher.

Lauren Thrift (9)
Grove Park CP School

A SIMILE

In my school I have;
A globe, as round as a football,
Pencil as light as a feather,
Books as if they were standing soldiers,
Homework as annoying as tidying rooms.

My school is held together by;
Good behaviour like Christians,
Order like people in a queue,
Silence like Ninjas,
Teachers as wise as owls.

In my school I treasure;
Friendship as precious as gold,
Technology as fun as football,
Knowledge, as vast as the ocean,
Security, like a mother holding a baby.

Christopher Jenkins (10)
Grove Park CP School

THE SKY

T   he sky up there, clouds resting on his vast chest
H   e is always changing from blue to black
      then to black and white
E   veryone thinks he's best

S   hining on through its invisible neck
K   eeping a watch on the Earth
Y   ear by year the sun shines down on us.

Ross Faulkner (10)
Lansdowne CP School

MONSTER UNDER MY BED

There's a monster under my bed,
And I know it.
It feeds on dirty socks and underwear.
Mum said, 'Whatever.'
Dad said, 'Imagination.'
My brother said, 'Yeah right.'

Mum, Dad and my brother
Came in my room last night,
They saw the monster eating me,
Then it fled and was never seen again.

But it had a baby,
And it will rein again!
There was a monster under my bed,
And there will be soon!

Emily Middleton (10)
Lansdowne CP School

FEELINGS

F eelings are for caring
E ars are for listening to other people's problems
E veryone I know has feelings
L ike me!
I is for I know I can trust you
N asty feelings, naughty feelings
G reat amazement!
S ad feelings, happy feelings!

Kim Wilson (10)
Lansdowne CP School

TEACHER

T   errible, terrible is Mr Stembridge,
E   very day I face my fear.
A   gonisingly I face my terror,
C   runching is our teacher's voice.
H   orrors! Horrors! I dream of him.
E   verlasting days, they seem to be.
R   ushing for the exit to escape. From! From!
S   chool, I dread it, curse M . . . M . . . Mr Stembridge.

Lewis Jordan (10)
Lansdowne CP School

RAINBOW

R ain and the sun make colourful rainbows
A nd I just love looking at all the colours
I   just stare out the window, it looks so beautiful,
N obody hates rainbows. I don't, do you?
B lue sky with the rainbow across it.
O h I wish there was a rainbow every day
W ait! I want to say goodbye before it goes.

Charlotte Joseph (8)
Lansdowne CP School

THE NOISE OF DEAFNESS

N othing!
O ut of the whole world someone must be able to hear me
I   t can't be that hard, can it?
S oundless, help me please.
E choes of my thoughts travel around my head.

Terri Wood (10)
Lansdowne CP School

SWIMMING

When I go swimming I think I might be a dolphin!
But then I remember I have no fins

When I go swimming I think I might be a shark!
But then I remember I'm not that sharp

When I go swimming there will be laughing and splashing
And I know that it will be smashing.

Andrew Kierans (7)
Lansdowne CP School

THE STORM

Stormy days in every way
Delivering in every tray,
Time to sleep on stormy nights,
Open shops in the night,
Read and write
We fight and might
And we like to try.

Jessica Bennett (8)
Lansdowne CP School

WHAT TEACHERS WEAR IN BED

What teachers wear in bed
is a mystery to me.
Underwear, or even bare.
I've always wanted to see.

Dean Moon (10)
Lansdowne CP School

SNOW

S un glistening snow crystals so crisp beneath my feet
N ever have I seen so much, this really is a treat!
O ver the hills I ride my sleigh and squeal with great delight
W oollen hats and mittens keeping me warm,
     I might really look a sight.
Y et I wouldn't have missed this for anything,
     I've had the best time of my life,

D amp, wet and cold, I plod on home for tea,
A nything hot will do for me,
     I'm chilled right through my bones.
Y our bath is waiting first my love, to keep blue cold out
S oaking away the day's winter chills,
     I've had a fantastic day and that's without a doubt!

Claire Hurn (7)
Lansdowne CP School

THIS LUMP OF CAKE

This lump of cake waits
     in the fridge.
This lump of cake has
     to be eaten.
This lump of cake must be
     eaten by me!
My mouth is watering.
Click! The fridge is open.
I dive for the plate . . .
Aaaah! I sink my teeth into
     the velvety icing,
'This is paradise', I think!

Louise Ralph (10)
Lansdowne CP School

TIGERS

Tigers are wild creatures
You can draw them as funny features!
You could sketch one eating,
Or maybe even sleeping!

Tigers might sleep all day,
But that would be okay!
They might bite,
And it would hurt.

Tigers have whiskers,
They might have brothers and sisters,
They might have one or the other,
Or some might not have any.

Zoe Drury (8)
Lansdowne CP School

DOLPHIN

Splash,
As I dive into the sea.
Swoosh,
As I swerve past rocks.
Splosh,
I see a big juicy fish.
Round I go again
I jump up to the sky.
As the sun shines on me
My skin goes shimmery.
Splash,
As I dive back into the sea.

Demi Whiskin (10)
Lansdowne CP School

WAVES

The waves, a man's fist beating the sand,
I'm standing here waiting on solid land,
The wind's slashing my face like a knife,
Holding me back from its clutches, saving my life,
The seagull's calling, calling for me,
The sea's disastrous, a disastrous sea,
I'm standing here waiting on solid land,
Hoping and hoping it will lay peacefully on the sand.

Chloë Williams (10)
Lansdowne CP School

DOLPHINS

Dolphins are beautiful,
They never bite you,
They help you sometimes if you drown,
They sing to you.

They make you happy sometimes,
They make you happy when you are sad.

Danielle Stickells (8)
Lansdowne CP School

DOWN BEHIND THE DUSTBIN

Down behind the dustbin
I meet a dog called Becky
I said to her, 'What are you doing?'
She said, 'I'm eating a bowl of spaghetti!'

Rebecca Thurston (10)
Lansdowne CP School

RABBITS

R   ather like a hare,
A   rabbit will need a lot of care
B   ecause they are small,
B   ecause they are carefree,
I   want you to love them all,
T   o you they need friendship.
S   o take care of them

All!

Andrea Glass (10)
Lansdowne CP School

SOUND

S   omebody must be able to hear me
O   ur lives are all different
U   nderstanding me can't be that hard,
    can it?
N   o one would like to be deaf like me.
D   oes anyone like me?

Louise Smith (11)
Lansdowne CP School

THE HORSE

The horse, chestnut and brown
Looks very down
But when his rider comes to play.
Now what do you say
The horse, chestnut and brown is very happy.

Hollie Parkinson (8)
Lansdowne CP School

UNDERWEAR

U nder your trousers they live or on your chest
N obody knows how or why they are there
D ifferent underwear is there every day
E ven your parents don't know how they get there
    or even your grandparents
R otting if you like 'em is difficult
W ould you vote for underwear to be banned? I wouldn't
E very day you or me, we have to cope with them
A fter you finally get them off they just hop back on
R eally, would you like to wear underwear?

Daniel Neville (10)
Lansdowne CP School

MY BROTHERS

My brothers are stupid!
My brothers are Kevins!
My brothers make me mad!
My brothers eat my sweets!
My brothers play tricks on me!
My brothers have no manners!
My brothers make a mess!
My brothers wrecked my room!
My brothers wrecked my toys!
My brothers can be very mean!
My brothers can snore!
But they are my brothers
And I really do love them!
Sometimes!

Avril Cooper (7)
Lansdowne CP School

WEATHER

Drip, drop, drip, drop,
Here comes the rain,
Drip, drop, drip, drop,
On the windowpane.

                    Sunshine, sunshine,
                    Out comes the sun.
                    Sunshine, sunshine,
                    Fun for everyone.

Rainbow, rainbow,
Colours all bright,
Rainbow, rainbow,
What a beautiful sight.

Megan Clark (11)
Lansdowne CP School

SEA FEVER

S   hips sink in the storm
E   nemies destroy ships
A   fter battles wood gets scattered

F   orever souls are restless
E   ven sharks are scared
V   icious sealife is even scared
E   ncounters with killer whales
     are destructive
R   emaining parts of ships
     are scattered everywhere.

Conor Harris (11)
Lansdowne CP School

YELLOW

Yellow is as bright and as beautiful
as golden corn blowing in the wind

Yellow as yellow as pollen
in a new spring flower.

Yellow is as bright and as light as
the sun beating down at the ground,

As yellow as a buttercup dancing in the sun,

Yellow as a ripe lemon
as sharp as a bee sting

As yellow as a curved banana
ripe and ready to eat.

Georgina Brady (10)
Lansdowne CP School

THE LONELY SINK

In the fun-filled classroom lies the lonely sink,
Frail and lifeless, old and used.
Dark and dingy, chipped and bruised.
In the fun-filled classroom lies the lonely sink.
Glue stuck to the bottom, cleaned for many years.
Full of children's fingerprints, paint and dirty smears.
In the fun-filled classroom lies the lonely sink.
Covered in splashes of dirty paint.
Look, your reflection's very faint.

Nula Clark (9)
Lansdowne CP School

SOUND OF SILENCE

S is for *soundless*
O is for a switch turned *off!*
U is for *utter* silence.
N is for *nothing!*
D is for a *dim* candle ready to be burned out.

O is for someone to *obtain* my hearing
F is for *forever* deafness.

S is for *screaming* children
I is for *isolated* hearing
L is for no *loudness*
E *verything* is misty
N is for *no one* there!
C is to make me *calm* - if I can!
E *verybody*, please help me hear again!

Adam Briggs (11)
Lansdowne CP School

HAMSTERS

H amsters are such cute little things
A s they scuttle around in their cages,
M ine is a Chinese dwarf hamster.
S ome of them just come out for food
T ime will pass as they grow and grow
E ach of them have their own personality
R ight from the day they are born.
S o take care of them all!

Emma Barnaschone (11)
Lansdowne CP School

INVITATION

There is no reason I can see
Why anyone should visit me.
My house is very badly run
I sit too often in the sun.
My garden's full of wicked weeds,
And seldom gets the care it needs.

But at the moment there is treasure,
In which the caller may find pleasure,
The apple trees are bravely dressed
With pale pink blossom at its best,
And, in addition, you can see
Three kittens and a lilac tree.

These will not last - the kits will grow,
And apple blossom fall like snow.
I do not wish to ape my betters
And write you importuning letters,
But, if you're passing, come and see
The kittens and the lilac tree.

Vicky Loveridge (10)
Lansdowne CP School

SNOW

Snow, snow white as a polar bear.
Icicles that hang down like nails.
No, no, not those clothes, it's not summer.
Oh no, I've got this present already.
Grrrrrrrrrrrrrrrrrrrrrrrrrr.
Bells ringing because it's Christmas.

Jamie McKenna (7)
Lansdowne CP School

THE STONE FULL OF MEMORIES

The stone full of memories,
Memories from the sea,
Full of life,
Or full of death,
Whichever it may be.

The stone full of memories,
Memories from the sea,
Peachy-cream,
And stoney-grey,
Confusing it does seem.

The stone full of memories,
Memories from the sea,
Smells of fruit,
Smells of dirt,
A memory for *me*.

Ashleigh Wheeler (10)
Lansdowne CP School

IT'S NOT A BIRD

It flies very strongly, it's not a bird,
It's as long as a twig, it's not a bird,
It comes in many colours, it's not a bird,
It's timid and microscopic, it's not a bird,
It can hover in the air, it's not a bird,
It's not a bird, it's not a bee,
It's not a wasp, it's not a flea,
It's not a fly, it's a dragonfly.

Shane Finch (10)
Lansdowne CP School

FAT CAT

Fat
   Cat
      Take
         A
            Nap
         In
         The
      Midday
Sun
   Wash
      Behind
         Your
            Ears
               While
                  Napping
               On
         A
      Mat
   So
Sleepy
   Cat
      Had
         A
            Nap.

Martin Smith (9)
Lansdowne CP School

SPACE ENCOUNTER

Over the moon and far away,
The astronauts come out to play,
Floating in the dark starry sky,
What will they do if an alien flies by?

Will they scream, will they shout?
Will they wriggle and jump about?
Or will they simply float and stare
At this sight so very rare?

Eleanor Ashbee (10)
Lansdowne CP School

THE BEACH

T   he beach was a sandy place
H   eat shining on my face
E   ternal waves splashing pace by pace

B   ees buzzing past my head
E   ach and every one unfed
A   nd as I ambled through the sand
C   lutching pebbles in my hand
H   aving the time of my life.

Vicki Jones (10)
Lansdowne CP School

SPRING

Spring flowers poking through the ground
Rabbits hopping all around
Leaves are growing on the trees
Birds are flying in the breeze
Lambs are frolicking in the meadows
Horses peeping over the hedgerow.

Christina Trussler (7)
Lansdowne CP School

DARK

Darkness falls, I get scared as it presses against me
The moon casts pictures all around
Daggers stabbing, slashing,
Where am I? This isn't Earth.
Hands all around reaching trying to grab something.
What?
Is it me they want?
I must get out - but how?
Where can I escape
I'm so scared,
It arches its back and spits
It pounces, but missed -
Where is it?

Matt Lonsdale (11)
Lansdowne CP School

FOOL'S GOLD

Funny and strange is my rock
On the side is gold flakes like the Queen's frock
On the bottom edge is made up of silver speckles
Like the stars, like a bronze penny
It smells, it's like a rock from Mars.

Gold, silver, grey and brown
Is on my rock,
Loud sounds it makes if you drop it,
Crash, bang, boom goes my rock.

Anna Tong (10)
Lansdowne CP School

CHRISTMAS

I went out for Christmas dinner,
I had some roast pork,
We had a competition,
I wasn't the winner.

I saw Father Christmas,
I got a toy,
And then I worked out he
Was Uncle Roy.

On Boxing Day
I played with my brother,
He broke my video then another.

Andrew Hinson (8)
Lansdowne CP School

MY DAD

My dad is so silly
he dresses up as a woman
and runs around the village

My dad is so silly
he pretends to be a dog
and bites me, ouch!

My dad is so silly
he pretends to be an alien,
scary!

My dad is so silly
I get embarrassed.

Josh Ransley (9)
Lower Halstow CP School

I LOVE ANIMALS

I   love animals

L   ions sleep all day in the sun,
O   ctopus under the sea having fun,
V   ixen watching her cubs play,
E   lephants eat all day.

A   nimals are cute,
N   ightingales sing a beautiful song,
I   nsects like centipedes are very long,
M   onkeys jumping everywhere,
A   ntelope leaping here and there,
L   izards slithering all about,
S   ometimes hyenas shout.

That's why I love animals.

Anna Peaurt (9)
Lower Halstow CP School

MY DIRTY DAD

My dirty dad
he never washes.
My dirty dad
is so dirty.
My dirty dad
always has a mudbath.
My dirty dad
down the pub all day.
My dirty dad
never stops singing.
My dirty dad
sleeps out in a bin.

Jake Kirby Spree (10)
Lower Halstow CP School

THROUGH MY MAGIC DOOR

Through my magic door
The tall dark clock stands and strikes 12

Through my magic door
A bat flies high above me

Through my magic door
A vampire rises and starts his search

Through my magic door
A man-eating monster is groaning hungrily

Through my magic door
I wake up and see it was just a scary dream.

Victoria Oates (10)
Lower Halstow CP School

EVERY NIGHT WHEN I GO TO BED

I see a golden river swirling in my head
Every night when I go to bed
I see a colourful rainbow glistening in my head
Every night when I go to bed
I see a little yellow bird hovering in my head
Every night when I go to bed
I see white soft bunnies munching lime green grass
Every night when I go to bed
I see a furry squirrel slowly chomping nuts.

Danika Mennecillo (9)
Lower Halstow CP School

WHEN MY MIND RUNS WILD

When my mind runs wild
I do foolish things like
Scribble on the wall
And skid in the hall.

When my mind runs wild
I go madder than ever before
I dance about
And sometimes even prance around
And get laughed at by my friends.

When my mind runs wild
I do things I will regret
I would kick the cat
And sit on a rat
And then have to clean it up.

Rachel Kemp (10)
Lower Halstow CP School

CHOCOLATE

Chocolate is smooth.
Chocolate is scrumptious.
Chocolate is brown.
Chocolate is white.
I'll go to the shop
and buy a whole bag more
because I like chocolate.

David Burroughes (9)
Lower Halstow CP School

I HAD A POUND COIN

I had a pound coin
Walked round the block

I walked straight into a baker's shop
I bent down to have a look

I put my hand on the cabinet and it shook
I stood back up and scratched my head

I looked at her and then I said,
'Please can I have a doughnut for tea?'
I handed her the coin she said, 'Here let me see.'

'This coin is no good for me
It has a hole, it goes straight through,'
Says I, 'The doughnut has too.'

Jimmy Farrelly (11)
Lower Halstow CP School

HAIRY SPIDERS

Hairy spiders have lots of legs
They love to climb in people's beds
In the corner on the door
They love to creep across the floor
Some are big, some are small
But some don't exist at all.
Some are hairy,
Some are scary.

Kirsty Warren (10)
Lower Halstow CP School

WHY IS IT WHEN I WALK . . .

Why is it when I walk under
a tree
all the plums and apples fall
on me?

Why is it when I walk under
a tree
all the birds come out and
peck me?

Why is it when I hide under
a tree
everybody ends up seeing
me?

Why is it when I walk under
a tree
it always starts pouring
on me?

Oh that tree does annoy me,
I'll chop it down
you wait and see!

Carrie-Anne Kemp (9)
Lower Halstow CP School

I LOVE MY CATS

I love my cats
they are cute and sweet

I love my cats
but they always eat
big chunks of meat

I love my cats
they curl up on your lap

I love my cats
and they always have
time to nap

I love my cats
they are the very best

I love my cats
they are far better
than the rest

I love my cats
they never go far

I love my cats
the exact way they are!

Nicola Gilfrin (11)
Lower Halstow CP School

I'M LOOKING FOR A FRIEND

I'm looking for a friend
Someone smart and rich

I'm looking for a friend
Someone with a bike

I'm looking for a friend
Someone true and free

I'm looking for a friend
Someone just like me

I'm looking for a friend
Someone really new

I'm looking for a friend
Someone really clever

That special kind of person
Might perhaps be you.

Matthew Buckingham (9)
Lower Halstow CP School

WHEN I GO TO SLEEP

When I go to sleep,
A zombie lies downstairs in a heap

When I go to sleep,
My dad becomes a werewolf in his sleep

When I go to sleep
Ghostly pirates guard whatever they keep

When I go to sleep
A vampire makes me get out of bed with a leap

When I go to sleep,
All the floorboards start to creak

When I go to sleep,
The chain on a ghost rattles as he goes for a creep

When I wake up from my sleep,
My alarm goes off with a beep, beep.

Craig Coppack (9)
Lower Halstow CP School

MY CATS NEVER SIT STILL

My cats never sit still
because they are always
running around the house
as if they have seen a mouse.

My cats never sit still
because they are always
fighting and knocking things
off the window sill.

My cats never sit still
because they are always
hungry but when we feed
them they are still hungry

My cats never sit still
because they always
claw the settee when
we are eating our tea.

I love my cats
just the way they are.

Amy Arnold (10)
Lower Halstow CP School

THE THIRTEENTH CLOCK

When the thirteenth clock
strikes the thirteenth hour
spiders weave their glinting webs

When the thirteenth clock
strikes the thirteenth hour
black bats flutter onto
the rustic gravestones.

When the thirteenth clock
strikes the thirteenth hour
skeletons dance gleefully
upon their graves.

When the thirteenth clock
strikes the thirteenth hour
vampires rise to find fresh blood.

When the thirteenth clock
strikes the thirteenth hour
the gilt sun rises to find
a normal and silent graveyard.

Laura Varney (10)
Lower Halstow CP School

IN MY SPECIAL SWEETY WORLD

In my special sweety world
Caramel streams flow down the hill

In my special sweety world
Dark and white chocolate people
Walk along the streets

In my special sweety world
Smarties roll along the road

In my special sweety world
Houses made of sticky toffee

In my special sweety world
People drink hot chocolate happily

In my special sweety world
I wake up and find out
That it was only a dream!

William Oates (10)
Lower Halstow CP School

MY BIG BROTHER THINKS

My big brother thinks
he can run like a cheetah.

My big brother thinks
he's on Top Of The Pops playing a banjo.

My big brother thinks
he's Buzz Lightyear flying across the galaxy.

My big brother thinks
he's Harry Potter whizzing round on his broomstick

My big brother thinks
he's Spiderman webbing people up

And my big brother thinks
he's Chris Tarrant on Who Wants To Be A Millionaire.

'Hu, hu!'

Tony Still (11)
Lower Halstow CP School

EVERY BORING DAY WHEN I WAKE UP . . .

Every boring day when I wake up
I hear my big sister Holly moaning,
'Where's my school bag?'

Every boring day when I wake up
I hear my mum shouting,
'Your breakfast is on the table.'

Every boring day when I wake up
I think about the dreams I had,
Which are always nice.

Every boring day when I wake up
I hear my dad going to work in his big blue van.

Every boring day when I wake up
I go downstairs and my mum's moaning at me,
Saying, 'Hurry up and get ready for school!'

Esme Fenner-Loftus (9)
Lower Halstow CP School

THE GHOST OF COLIN MCSHOOR

As the light dims,
And the night begins,
And the wind whistles over the moor,
From behind a bush appears the ghost of Colin McShoor.

Over the treetops he rides,
Through the town he glides,
Up to Primrose House,
In he sneaks quiet as a mouse.

Where little children sleep,
He does lurk and he does creep,
Right to the smallest boy's room,
The ghost comes to bring doom.

Slowly the sun does rise,
Burning out his eyes,
To the moor he is banished then,
But tomorrow night he'll rise again.

Lucy Cowburn (11)
Lower Halstow CP School

IN MY SECRET HAUNTED CHAMBER

In my secret haunted chamber
Bats flutter through dusty windows
In my secret haunted chamber
The owls screech in the midnight air
In my secret haunted chamber
The cold misty moon gazes through the window
In my secret haunted chamber
Witches fly in a starry sky
In my secret haunted chamber
Wind whistles through a creaky tree
In my secret haunted chamber
Chains rattle and stairs creak
In my secret haunted chamber
A chill goes down my spine
In my secret haunted chamber
The clock strikes twelve and the ghost party begins!

Paul Hood (10)
Lower Halstow CP School

I CLOSE MY EYES

I close my eyes and I can see
Smarties falling from the sky.

I close my eyes and I can see
Zombies going to chase me, help!

I close my eyes and I can see
Green slimy aliens attacking the world.

I close my eyes and I can see
Ghosts scaring people.

I close my eyes and I can see
Mum trying to wake me up,
'Breakfast!'

Lewis Church (11)
Lower Halstow CP School

ELVES

Elves might seem happy, fun and filled with delight,
but when they enter the misty midnight
they're not all they seem.
They attack and are ready to bite,
they wear a dark scarlet, velvet cape and once you
are underneath it you may never escape.
They have teeth as sharp as needles can be
and once they have bitten into you, you cannot flee.
The tastiest place for them to feed on is the knee!

It makes you feel sick doesn't it
to think of all of that blood-red runny stuff,
all of that goo!

Kirsty Ferguson (11)
Lower Halstow CP School

MY CRAZY MUM

My crazy mum
My mum, she's a lazy one
  My crazy mum
My mum, she's a crazy one
  My crazy mum
When I'm bad she gets mad
  My crazy mum
We know who's boss
  My crazy mum
When she gets cross
  My crazy mum
Although she's nuts
  My crazy mum
I love her lots
Because to me she's tops.

Daniel Parker (9)
Lower Halstow CP School

WATER LIFT-OFF

Waves,
flume,
locker,
floats,
chlorine,
slide,
blue,
water,
cold,
clean.

Rebecca Reed (9)
Minterne County Junior School

KYLE

Kyle is my best friend.
When I'm sad he comes to cheer me up,
So Kyle is my best friend because he's friendly.

I like Kyle because he's kind to me
And most of all friendly.
I like Kyle because he's always got a big smile.
I like Kyle because he supports West Ham.

Jake Brissenden (8)
Minterne County Junior School

SCHOOL

S   chool is boring,
C   lass is always messy,
H   ome is brilliant,
O   dear, I forgot my stuff,
O   dear, I'm late,
L   azy teachers sit in their chairs.

Shane Priston (8)
Minterne County Junior School

MY DAD SAYS

My dad says,
Don't be mad,
Don't throw your tea at the wall,
Don't kick your brother,
Don't lick the lamp post.
Please don't do it at home.

Lewis Tumber (8)
Minterne County Junior School

ANIMALS

A lligators like the water,
N esting birds have their babies,
I nsects are always getting squashed,
M onkeys swing through the trees,
A nimals are amazing things,
L ittle ones especially,
S o many animals, I like them all.

George Luther (8)
Minterne County Junior School

MY CAT BARLEY

My cat lives in my bedroom,
He sleeps on my bed at night.
Every morning I come downstairs
And feed my cat.
Every morning and every afternoon.

Alice Hughes (9)
Minterne County Junior School

THE SPIDER

There is a really big spider
Who swings from here to there.
He makes silver webs everywhere he goes.
Poor old spider,
He's been squashed by a foot.

Glen Thomson (9)
Minterne County Junior School

THE GRANNY WITH AN UMBRELLA

There was an old granny
who was thin and skinny
and she had a colourful umbrella.

So I went to this old granny and said,
'Please may I have a look at your umbrella?'

'Did you say you wanted to look at my umbrella?'
'Yes.'
So the granny got her umbrella
and whacked, smacked and slapped the old boy
on his back.

No wonder people don't come to this granny.
She's mad and crazy and whacks people.

Aimee Patrick (8)
Minterne County Junior School

ADULTS

I wish I was an adult,
tall and big and strong.
Everyone would admire me
and I could do what I wanted!

I wish I was an adult,
brave and bold and super.
Everyone would think I'm cool,
and I wouldn't have to go to school!

But sometimes I think it's best to be a child,
because I don't have to pay the bills
or go to work, all the time.

Zoë Blogg (9)
Minterne County Junior School

MY MUM SAYS

My mum says,
'Don't point.
Don't punch.
Don't kick.
Don't put your elbow on the table.
Don't be cruel.
Go upstairs.
Don't be silly.
Don't pick your nose.
Be good and be nice.'

My mum says,
'Be polite and very
Kind to your friends.
Don't kiss your girlfriend at night.
Walk away,' says my mum.

Stephen Jacobs (9)
Minterne County Junior School

GHOST TRAIN

I've never seen a ghost train
That makes people frown.
I don't like this ghost train,
It's creepy and it's very dark,
To hide bats in the night.
They stay in there every day,
Then come back and say,
'I don't like ghosts,
I'm all alone,
So that means I want to go home.'

Adam Green (8)
Minterne County Junior School

MONEY

Daddy said money doesn't grow on trees.
Mummy said money doesn't grow on me.
      So where does it grow?

I looked in my dictionary,
But it only said it came from the Royal Mint,
      But isn't this mint a sweet?

Anthony West (10)
Minterne County Junior School

SEASIDE

S   parkling water at the beach,
E   ating ice-cream (yummy),
A   nice day at the seaside.
S   uper sunsets if you stay long enough,
I   ncredible suntan from the sun,
D   ecent water,
E   xciting nightlife.

Samantha Oliver (9)
Minterne County Junior School

TIME

T   he Romans did invade,
I   could see them fight,
M   ight they win,
E   very time we win.

Robert Mills (8)
Minterne County Junior School

MY PET

My pet is furry,
My pet is soppy,
My pet is smelly,
My pet is cuddly,
My pet follows me,
My pet is cool,
My pet fetches sticks.
Can you guess my pet?

Ian Kingsman (9)
Minterne County Junior School

SPRING

S   kipping lambs in the fields!
P   retty flowers shimmering in the sun,
R   avens eating breadcrumbs.
I   just want to have fun.
N   ibbling rabbits eating grass,
G   olden daffodils looking like trumpets.

Georgina Winney (9)
Minterne County Junior School

SCHOOL

S   chool is for learning things,
C   oach the team to play football.
H   ot and spicy, lovely curry.
O   ur uniform is the best in the world,
O   ur sports are the best in Kent.
L   ovely stars are waiting to go in your book.

Fiona Cordes (9)
Minterne County Junior School

FOOD LIFT-OFF

Cake,
beans,
eggs,
peas,
crisps,
bread,
biscuits,
chocolate,
fish fingers,
peanut butter,
cream crackers.

Johnathon Ralph (9)
Minterne County Junior School

ROCKET FOOD

Curry,
soup,
roast,
toast,
fruit,
crisps,
tomato,
potato,
chocolate,
sick a lot.

Kirstie Macmaster (8)
Minterne County Junior School

BODY TAKE-OFF

Ears,
eyes,
teeth,
ribs,
tummy,
mouth,
eyelids,
brain,
nose,
fingers.

Alice Bonney (9)
Minterne County Junior School

SWIMMING POOL BLAST-OFF

Fun,
floats,
flumes,
deep,
cold,
slides,
diving,
lockers,
big wave,
splash!

Chloe Fosbraey (8)
Minterne County Junior School

WEATHER IS NICE

W hen it rains
E verybody is
A ngry.
T hen a
H urricane comes,
E verybody
R uns away.

I n England it is
S ometimes sunny.

N early spring,
I ce is gone,
C reatures walking in the sun,
E xcited people are happy.

Arron O'Grady (9)
Minterne County Junior School

COMPLAINING

I can't stop
Complaining, complaining
About my brother complaining
About me.
So should I
Complain about him
Or not?
You know,
So tell me,
Because I don't.

Christian Collins (8)
Minterne County Junior School

MY FAVOURITE ICE CREAM

I like the flavour of . . .
Strawberries, blueberries, old berries, new berries.
I like the type of . . .
On cones, in cones, small cones, big cones.
I like the sprinkles of . . .
Chocolate fudge, or lots of crunched up nuts.
I like it in a . . .
Coloured wrapper, tall wrapper, big wrapper, small wrapper.
Can you guess what it is?
I'm glad you asked.
A Cornetto.
Oops, I dropped it!

Cassie Glenn (8)
Minterne County Junior School

SPIDERS

I love spiders,
Big ones, small ones,
Thin ones, fat ones,
I love spiders,
I love putting them
Down the back of Nan's jumper.
I love spiders in jars,
Spiders on walls,
Even spiders in the bath,
The bigger they are the more I like them.
I like spiders.
Best of all, I like standing on them!

Oliver Halls (11)
Minterne County Junior School

THE GHOST

The ghost lived in a dark, dark house,
With a dark, dark door and a dark, dark room.
He goes through the dark, dark walls,
Into the dark, dark closet.
There are two skeletons in the closet.
'Boo' said the ghost,
'We're scared,' said the skeletons.
'Let's run.'

Charlie Kavanagh (9)
Minterne County Junior School

CROSS!

C rackling shouts!
R ummaging under the quilt,
O uch!
S itting on the chair, crying,
S o don't spoil the image of *cross!*

Emily Blackwell (8)
Minterne County Junior School

PETS

P ets are cool,
E veryone loves dogs,
T wo cats sleeping,
S ome pets live in cages.

Amy Adlington (9)
Minterne County Junior School

FOOTBALL BLAST-OFF

Brazil,
Everton,
Bradford,
Chelsea,
Ipswich,
Gillingham,
Arsenal,
West Ham,
Liverpool,
Crystal Palace.

Kieran Taylor (8)
Minterne County Junior School

SPORTS IN SPACE

Tennis,
Golf,
Ping-pong,
Rugby,
Running,
Swimming,
Football,
Judo,
Karate,
Olympic sports!

Lloyd Waghorn (9)
Minterne County Junior School

FOOD WITH A BANG!

Beans,
Ham,
Peaches,
Ice-cream,
Apple,
Soup,
Duck,
Beef,
Carrots,
Gravy.
Food!

Lucy Todd (8)
Minterne County Junior School

CRAZY CREATURES

Pigs,
Dogs,
Bears,
Frogs,
Seals,
Cats,
Horses,
Rats,
Penguins,
Tigers.

Matthew Knell (9)
Minterne County Junior School

WEATHER BLAST-OFF

Frosty,
chilly,
icy,
sunny,
cloudy,
hot,
sunshine,
thunder,
scared,
storm,
thunder and lightning.

James Smith (8)
Minterne County Junior School

BONY ROCKET

Brain,
spine,
bone,
head,
blood,
legs,
heart,
ear,
eyes,
Adam's apple.

James Watson (9)
Minterne County Junior School

RULES, RULES, RULES

Rules, rules, rules,
Don't jump in muddy water pools.
Rules, rules, rules,
Don't run through the halls.

Teachers, teachers, teachers,
They're very much like preachers.
Teachers, teachers, teachers,
In the staffroom they drink tea like bloodsucking leeches.

After school they stand there fagging,
I hate their nagging.
I want to run away from school, break all the rules
And jump in a muddy pool.

Nathan Temple (10)
Minterne County Junior School

UNTITLED

A ghost lives in my cellar.
At night it makes big bangs and crashes,
He thumps walls
And makes ghost noises.
It turns the TV on
And the radio at full blast.
He blows the big speakers,
Then he runs the bath.
He picks up the false teeth in the bathroom.

Kingsley Currie (9)
Minterne County Junior School

MY FAVOURITE JUMPER

My jumper is all blue and scraggy,
And on me it is quite baggy.

Mum always tells me to roll up my sleeves,
But what do I care she doesn't say please.

My sister tells me my jumper's junk,
So I tell my mum and she goes off in a hump.

My dad tells me that it's got to go,
But I just say, 'So.'

So that's what they think of my jumper you see.
But no one can take my jumper from me.

Harriet Burns (11)
Minterne County Junior School

MY FAMILY

My sister is a big fat blister,
She sleeps in her jammys
And thinks she'll win Grammys.
My cousin's worse,
She thinks she'll never ride in a hearse.
My mum is a lot of fun,
She sometimes puts my hair in a bun.
My dad said boo hoo,
When he got a tattoo.
And as for me,
I seem to agree with all this madness.

Hayley Beard (11)
Minterne County Junior School

THE UNFORMABLE DOG

One day in my back garden,
I found a lonely dog.
When I rubbed his back,
He changed into a hog!

He was wearing a pair of glasses
That looked rather funky.
I rubbed his back again,
He changed into a monkey!

He had brown hair that was spiky
And climbed my house.
I rubbed his back for the third time,
He changed into a mouse!

He had pink ears
And was as big as a jeep.
I rubbed his ears this time,
He changed into a sheep!

Something fell out of the sky,
It was a key.
I rubbed him between the ears,
He turned into a Mercedes!

I opened the door
And got into the car.
I put the key into the ignition
And drove afar.

Anand Sahota (11)
Minterne County Junior School

ME AND MY MUM

When I was one I loved my mum
and my mum loved me too.
When I was two I tied my shoe
and my mum said 'that was good.'
When I was three I banged my knee
and my mum kissed it better.
When I was four I fell on the floor
and my mum picked me up.
When I was five I saw a beehive
but my mum told me not to go close.
When I was six I picked up some sticks
and carried them to my mum.
When I was seven I thought I was in Heaven
but my mum told me I wasn't.
When I was eight I had a special plate
that my mum had bought me for my birthday.
When I was nine I drank some wine
out of my mum's cup.
But now I'm ten and I've seen Big Ben.
I'm looking on to the future.

Emily Crutchley (10)
Minterne County Junior School

GHOST

4G houlish ghosts floating throughout the house,
H   orrible spirit, that describes a ghost,
O   ur ghost will make you scream.
S   lowly sliding under my door,
T   rying to scare me, but I'm fast asleep.

Joseph Bowerman (8)
Minterne County Junior School

AN ALIEN'S VISIT

An alien came to my house yesterday,
I told him to go away,
Instead he barged right in,
And started eating what's in the bin.

He ate the fridge contents and all,
He ran up the stairs and had a great fall,
He got in his spaceship,
And flew, flew away.

He went past stars,
And landed on Mars,
He went through his door,
And smelt wild boar.

He went to the kitchen,
Where his wife was cooking,
He said, 'That smells nice,'
And asked for some rice.

He ate it all,
And said he was full.
And with that he went to bed,
And hit his head.

Peter Easton (10)
Minterne County Junior School

STARLIGHT

Starlight, starlight, glittering so high,
Peaking through my window late at night.
When I go to sleep,
I always think
'What a beautiful sight.'

Starlight, starlight, shining through the night,
Brighter than any other light.
When I wake up,
I always think,
'What happened last night?'

Peter Terry (9)
Minterne County Junior School

WHO IS THAT?

Who is that by the door
Biting its toes,
Scratching the floor?
Maybe the cat,
Maybe the rat,
Maybe my friend Maggie fat!
Who knows!

Who is that swimming in dirt
Washing its feet,
Wearing its shirt?
Maybe it's Ami,
Maybe it's Jami,
Maybe my friend Hairy Hayley!
Who knows!

Who is that lying in bed
Resting its eyes
Is it dead?
Maybe it's Fred,
Maybe it's Led,
Maybe it's my friend Coconut Head!
Who knows!

Jordan Tydeman (10)
Minterne County Junior School

THERE'S A THINGY IN MY THING

'There's a thingy in my thing.'
'What's a thingy?'
'Well, it's green and slimy, gooey and really ugly!'
'Wow, what does it eat?'
'Well, it eats worms and spiders and mouldy bread
        and stale yoghurts and black bananas.'
'Wow!'

'There's a thingy in my thing.'
'What's a thing?'
'Well, it's big and warm and cosy.'
'Wow!'

Declan Douglas (10)
Minterne County Junior School

LINK'S ADVENTURE

In a world transformed by evil
There lived a young boy named Link
Who found himself fighting for its very existence.
He tracked down Majora, the evil entity,
To face its two transformations,
Majora's incarnation and Majora's wrath.
With guilded sword in hand
And the mirror shield for protection,
He struck down the fearsome monstrosity.
After the final sword stroke against Majora,
The world returned to normal,
With Link proclaimed the hero.

Christopher Wilson (11)
Minterne County Junior School

AN ALIEN'S GOT MY T-SHIRT

A spaceship came down last night
And landed in my garden,
The spaceship made a wooing sound
And out popped a little alien.
He tried to ring the doorbell
But nothing happened,
So he jumped through the window.
He came up to my bedroom
But didn't knock on the door,
He rummaged through my drawers
And pulled out a T-shirt.
The alien jumped out of the window,
He jumped into the spaceship.
I wonder where he is now?

Andrew Kitney (11)
Minterne County Junior School

WORLD WAR 3

World War 3 started the other day
When my friend came over to play.
At first we were having a lot of fun
But when the clock began to chime at one
At first we were having a great big laugh
But then she ripped my toy giraffe.
'You stupid thing! You fool!' I yelled.
And then pushed her on the ground.
She screamed and cried,
Then wiped her eyes
And kicked me in my shin.
The teacher came out yelling, 'What's that din?'
And now we are in big trouble!

Lucy Gallagher (10)
Minterne County Junior School

THE STORM

Bing, bang, boom.
What on earth is going on?
Flash, crash, smash,
What's gone wrong?
Lightning clashes in the air.
I peep through the curtains,
What's going on?
Wind rumbles and bumbles through the stormy sky.
Smash, crash, bang.
What's going on now?
A storm of course,
But I am safe inside.

Kirsty Rogers (11)
Minterne County Junior School

LIFT-OFF

Wet,
cold,
shallow,
deep,
soft,
hot,
waves,
warm,
blue,
fun,
splash!

Thomas Sales (8)
Minterne County Junior School

THE TOILET MONSTER

There's a monster in our toilet,
who growls every time you flush.
And if you hear the toilet flushing,
you must rush to your bed as quickly as you can,
and dive under the covers.

If you don't make it to your bed in time,
the toilet monster may get you,
and pull you down the hole.

And if you want to attack the monster,
there's only one thing to use,
I know it probably won't work,
but the thing to use is a
Toilet cleaning brush!

Laura Wood (11)
Minterne County Junior School

MY PONY

I have a horse who's wonderful,
He's always happy and bright.
He has a brilliant nature
And his coat is soft and white.
I love to turn him out in the field
And watch him gallop around.
He's covered in mud when I get him in,
So I groom him until no mud can be found,
Then put him in his stable and
Settle him down for the night.

Megan Bartlet (10)
Minterne County Junior School

LATE FOR SCHOOL

I'm not allowed to be late for school,
My teacher says it's a school rule.
I sprint into the classroom at 9.02,
Oh no, I'm late, what am I going to do?
I sit down in my place at 9.03,
'Stephanie Hyams come to me.'
He's shouting at me at 9.04,
He told me to stand outside the door,
The headmaster called my name,
I knew I was in trouble, but I wasn't to blame.
I got into more trouble as the day passed by,
I got into trouble for telling a lie.
Mum picked me up in her brand new Rover,
I had never been more pleased that school was over!

Stephanie Hyams (10)
Minterne County Junior School

GET SET, GO!

On your marks, get set, go!
I was running
There was a plop!
I was on my bum!
I got up
But carried on running
I was third
Then second
I had won!
My heart was beating
Like a frog jumping.

Claire Streatfield (10)
Minterne County Junior School

SCARED ABOUT MATHS?

I stand in the wooden doorway,
Clutching my books.
My knees are shaking rapidly.
I sit silently listening to the teacher,
The teacher stares at me, through her beady eyes.
She raises her chalk and does a
Long multiplication sum on the board,
She hands the chalk to me.
I stand up shaking,
I drop it!
She glares at me horribly,
I feel really awkward,
I've done the sum,
Yes, I've got it right.
The bell goes, yes, the lesson's over,
So this is the question -
Are you scared of maths?

Hollie Vallis (11)
Minterne County Junior School

CLEVER

People think they are cleverer than me,
But no, I am cleverer than them.
They are just jealous.
Sometimes they don't know the answer.
Nobody knows everything,
Except for me!
I know everything.
I know everything about the planet Earth.
Just because I'm *clever!*

Rebecca Simmons (11)
Minterne County Junior School

ONE DAY

One night I'd like to go to bed
and wake up calm, not feeling dread.
Without a worry I'd go and play
all my problems would melt away.
All the people everywhere that I know
are running free without a care.
No one sick, lame or ill, no need
to take an awful pill.
Just a dream? No this is real.
One day I know this for sure,
that peace will reign forever more.
One day . . .

Scott Barney
Minterne County Junior School

MY WRESTLER

When I hear a sound
Like ding, ding, I realise
to go to pin but
first wear him down
and then try to pin.

Then punch there, punch here
or kick there, kick here
then do moves like
Powerbomb or Tombstone,
then you go to pin then . . .
1 . . . 2 . . . 3 . . . the crowd go
mental, AJ, AJ, AJ!

Alex Betts (10)
Minterne County Junior School

FRIGHT IN THE NIGHT

'Time for bed.' My mother said.
So up the stairs to clean my teeth and brush my hair,

There I was lying there on my own reading
Fright in the Night,

All I could feel was my heart beat faster and faster,
What a disaster!

What was that?
It sounded like a clatter of plates.

Chatter, chatter, that's all I could hear,
Was it Mum?
Surely not!

Wouldn't she be asleep!
I could hear the bathroom tap dripping
with the beat of my heart.
What was that?

Sarah Harwood (10)
Minterne County Junior School

MY DOG

My dog laying there like a log.
Its pink tongue is like candyfloss.
White teeth as a plain book
Golden fur like a sun.
Chases cats as its favourite hobby.
It likes to eat cat food.
It loves her toys very much.

Jamie Ferris (11)
Minterne County Junior School

WHEN I WAS . . .

When I was 1
I saw my mum
For the first time

When I was 2
I sat on the loo
And went to the toilet

When I was 3
I saw a big tree
And it had blossom

When I was 4
I knocked on a door
And they said go away

When I was 5
I felt so alive
Because I went to a disco

When I was 6
I had some Tixylix
Because I had a sore throat

When I was 7
My pet went to Heaven
And I cried all the day

When I was 8
I went to a fete
And I saw my best friend

When I was 9
I looked fine
In my high heeled boots.

Now that I'm 10
And I have seen Big Ben
It's time to plan my future.

Jade Seamer (10)
Minterne County Junior School

STRANGE SOUNDS

When I walked down the town
I came across a daft looking cat.
Woof, woof,
How strange, a cat saying
Woof, woof.

I came to the park
I could see noisy birds not saying
Tweet, tweet,
But miaow, miaow,
What has happened,
I'm in a different world or even universe.

I saw a car go up to halt,
With a ring, ring,
And a bike screech
Cars and bikes too,
As well as birds and cats.

Luke Tumber (11)
Minterne County Junior School

CAT'S LIFE

It's just not fair being a cat,
You get told off and that is that!

My favourite is eating out of the bin,
Much more enjoyable than the tin.

I just help myself to a piece of toast,
Out of all the rubbish I like that the most.

When I need a little drink,
I simply jump up onto the sink.

I just love to see the water run
Sticking your paw in it is so much fun.

Time to play with my sister Lolly,
Sometimes she can be such a wally.

She always tries to give me a fright,
By giving me a slap to start a fight.

Later I get tired and I need a nap,
Somewhere warm but never a lap.

Under the radiator suits me just fine
A favourite spot of mine.

Victoria Bowerman (11)
Minterne County Junior School

DINNER TIME

Dinner time is the best time,
Except . . . when my brother starts mashing peas,
My dad starts chomping, and I . . .
Would rather just have some peace!

I love dinner,
Except . . . when I splat it on the floor.
It's not so nice because it's all dirty!
That's my dinner time.

Victoria Goodger (9)
Minterne County Junior School

THE FOOTBALL MATCH

Hustle, bustle push and shove,
In goes the ball but straight to the glove.
The whistle blows, another foul.
'Come on boys,' the parents howl.

The ball goes in this time for real,
Another graze that has to heal.
Two-nil up we're doing well,
The manager can't give us hell.

At half-time we take a drink,
We don't have a weakest link.
Our manager is full of praise,
It makes a change from his usual raves.

Back on we go, it's going quick,
The other team is looking sick.
We run around full of skill,
We're going to win at least two-nil!

The whistle blows for full time,
Up the table we will climb.
We're at the top, our team's the best,
We'll all go home to a well earned rest.

Liam Golchehreh (11)
Minterne County Junior School

THE RAIN

The rain is wet and cold,
It drips on me like I am
going for a shower.
It makes my skin wrinkle up
like a mouldy apple.
My clothes go soggy
like they've been in the
washing machine.
The rain is refreshing when
it runs in my mouth,
like drinking fresh milk
from a cow.
The puddles on the ground,
drip, drop, drip, drop,
like a tap dripping in the sink.
The rain is cold,
when it hits me it is like cold
snow being thrown at you.
I hate the rain, I really do,
I'd rather be in a jail reading
a book, safe from the *rain!*

Anthony Aldridge (10)
Minterne County Junior School

THE BRUSSEL SPROUT

There it lay, all green and round
Staring at me with no sound.
I poke it with my silver fork,
I'd rather have a piece of pork.

It looked just like a mushy pea,
Or a green eye which couldn't see.
There my dog sat on the ground,
She was making such a terrible sound.

I gave it to her as she sat very still,
She looked like she was going to be ill.
I went to my room as my mum called out,
'I've still got loads of Brussel sprouts.'

Jordan Buckner (10)
Minterne County Junior School

MY SISTER'S AN ALIEN

'Sam, Sam,' my sister called to me,
'I think I've seen a man from Mars,
He's come to look and see.
He may even be from distant stars.'

'Sam, Sam, please come and look.'
'Please Emily just let me sleep.'
'Sam, I can't find him any book.'
'Leave it Ems, it will keep.'

'Sam, I'm going in his spaceship!'
'Goodbye and have fun.'
'Just let me lay and kip.'
'Sam, now he's zapped me with his gun.'

There was a blinding flash,
He changed my sister to an alien,
Their teeth began to gnash,
It scared me so I began to waken.

The ship zoomed away,
I stood there all alone,
Whatever could I say?
Mum's sure to have a moan.

Sam Blackwell (11)
Minterne County Junior School

MY BABY BROTHER

My baby brother acts bigger than me,
He eats his food more properly.
He can put his own shoes on,
(He doesn't need me).
He says his room is private property.
He puts it up for sale every day and night.
He asks me to buy it, I say I might, might, might.
He rides his bike and hoots his horn,
Once he landed in a bunch of thorns.
So please, please, please make my brother like me!

Alice Evans (10)
Minterne County Junior School

WHAT IS RED?

What is red? A Ferrari is red
and Michael Schumacher led.
What is red? Stephanie's pen is red
in her bag instead.
 What is red? Blood is red
pumping round my head.
What is red? A falcon's red
when it's being fed.
What is red? Flames are red
that's what I thought someone said.
What is red? Cherryade is red
when I drank it in my bed.
What is red? My lawnmower is red
and I keep it in my shed.

Matthew Jewiss (10)
South Avenue Junior School

WHAT IS GREEN?

What is green?
Rustling leaves are green on a tree in the sky
so they can be seen.

What is green?
Apples are green, sweet and juicy, ready to be picked
then eaten when they are clean.

What is green?
Lettuce is green when you eat it with salad
with tomatoes in-between,

What is green?
A cucumber is green, to eat in your sandwich
with cheese so everyone is so keen,

What is green?
Grapes are green
juicy and round, that's what I mean.

Charlotte Tobin (9)
South Avenue Junior School

SCHOOL TIME

School is the time where you think and learn.
Creative English is my favourite subject.
Half-term is when you rest your brain and have a relaxation
              in the summer sun.
Oos and aas for funny poems to be written in beautiful
              handwriting.
Opening your mouth to shout out your answer to the sum.
Listen and learn from your teacher when she is explaining things.

Luke Edwards (10)
South Avenue Junior School

WHAT IS GREEN?

What is green?
A green crunchy bush is green,
Like a tree being blown by the wind.

What is green?
A yummy crunchy apple is green,
Being eaten like a pile of books fallen off a shelf.

What is green?
Solid juicy limes are like long blowy grass,
Just moving in the wind.

What is green?
Pencil cases are green,
As thick as a fluffy carpet.

What is green?
Big hard cardboard is green,
To hold our light green science folders.

What is green?
Fluffy pencil cases with a tail on the end,
'Uh, what do you mean?'

What is green?
Ryan's full packed lunch box is green,
And in it are some baked beans.

Gareth Messenger (9)
South Avenue Junior School

WHAT IS YELLOW?

What is yellow?
Stars are yellow,
As yellow as flashing flames in the dark.
What is yellow?
The bright sun is yellow,
Melting us like a flame melting a candle.
What is yellow?
Lights are yellow,
Shining brightly like crystals in our eyes.
What is yellow?
Bananas are yellow,
Big and fat like a pregnant lady's belly.
What is yellow?
Eagle's house team are yellow,
Winning nearly every sports day.
What is yellow?
Corn is yellow,
Covering the big fields.
What is yellow?
Custard is yellow,
Lick the thick cream.
What is yellow?
Sand is yellow,
Bathing in the sun.

Emily Cooke (9)
South Avenue Junior School

Ten Dinosaurs

Ten dinosaurs having some wine
One got drunk then there were nine.

Nine dinosaurs bought some plates
One dropped his then there was eight.

Eight dinosaurs gone to Devon
One died then there were seven.

Seven dinosaurs having Weetabix
One choked then there were six.

Six dinosaurs looking at a beehive
One got stung then there were five.

Five dinosaurs were so poor
One was sick then there were four.

Four dinosaurs went to France and said, 'Wee!'
Then there were three.

Three dinosaurs were watching Doctor Who
One fell asleep then there were two.

Two dinosaurs dancing in the sun
One got burnt then there was one.

One dinosaur flew to Alaska and ate a bun
Then there were none.

Abusaem Shohid (9)
South Avenue Junior School

TEN LITTLE MICE

Ten little mice walking down the road,
one got pushed into a washing line,
then there were nine.
Nine little mice walking down the road,
one got stuck in a gate,
then there were eight.
Eight little mice walking down the road,
one rose up to Heaven,
then there were seven.
Seven little mice walking down the road,
one fell into a pile of sticks,
then there were six.
Six little mice walking down the road,
one walked into a beehive,
then there were five.
Five little mice walking down the road,
one chopped his finger off with a saw,
then there were four.
Four little mice walking down the road,
one walked into a tree,
then there were three.
Three little mice walking down the road,
one went to the loo,
then there were two.
Two little mice walking down the road,
one went to buy a bun, then there was one.
One little mouse walking down the road,
he fell on the floor,
so the mice were no more.

Benjamin Friedman (10)
South Avenue Junior School

WHAT IS BLUE?

What is blue?
Blue is runny ink,
On the paper soaking in.

What is blue?
Blue is freezing,
Making water transform to ice.

What is blue?
Blue tits are blue,
Chirping happily on a knobbly branch.

What is blue?
Blue is the sea,
With white ripples that canter towards the beach.

What is blue?
Bluebells are blue,
Swaying left and right in the gentle wind.

Sam Conway (9)
South Avenue Junior School

LONELINESS

Loneliness is grey,
It tastes like a broken heart and dull,
It sounds quite like nobody's around you,
It feels like a piece of white paper waiting to be written on,
It smells like the cold breeze pushing against my face.

Michael Palmer (10)
South Avenue Junior School

WHAT IS BLUE?

What is blue?
Bluebells are blue
They come out in spring and flower right throu'

What is blue?
The sea is blue
Violent and scary in a storm.

What is blue?
Some eyes are blue
Staring at you!

What is blue?
Midnight is blue
Stars shimmering in the sky.

What is blue?
Freezing is blue
Teeth chattering.

Lara Apps (10)
South Avenue Junior School

THE DOLPHINS THAT SAVED ME

D   o they understand people when they scream for help?
O   ver the waves they will come to save me
L   eaping through the air with water spurting out powerfully
P   assing through the mammoth waves rapidly
H   igh jumping over tidal waves so gently but rapidly
I   ntelligent and clever smart like a person and handsome
N   ever-ending life for dolphins
S   aved my life.

Latasha Armitage (11)
South Avenue Junior School

WHAT IS RED?

What is red?
Red is the smell of a
Freshly lit barbecue.

What is red?
Red is molten lava
Burning everything in its path.

What is red?
Red is hatred
Burning someone's mind.

What is red?
Red is a ruby
Being cast into gold.

What is red?
Red is a fiery
Dragon sleeping in a cave.

What is red?
Red is a rose much
Sharper than any thorn.

What is red?
Red is a fresh
Red Golden Delicious
Juicy and succulent
Waiting to be eaten.

What is red?
Red is my scarlet
Red jumper being
Hung on the line.

What is red?
Red is a fire engine
Zooming to the scene of a fire.

What is red?
Red is a fox
Hunting in the sun light.

What is red?
Red is a new
Blazing hot sun.

What is red?
Red is an
Overheated kettle.

Alex Brice (10)
South Avenue Junior School

WHAT IS BLUE?

What is blue?
The sea is blue when it is wavy.

What is blue?
My team is blue, like birds flying in the sky.

What is blue?
The sky is blue,
The sky is blue with clouds all bunched up too.

What is blue?
Our board is blue showing rules and house points too.

What is blue?
Colouring is blue on a birthday cake for you.

What is blue?
My friend's pen is blue.

Liam Taylor (9)
South Avenue Junior School

WHITE

White is as white as clouds, drifting through the cool windy sky.
White is as white as a sheet of paper lying still, waiting to be drawn on.
White is as white as talcum powder settling all over you making you
covered in this soft powdery snow.
White is as white as a light switch ready to be pushed so that light will
come surging through a white light bulb.
White is as white as a wall ready to have thick paint splattered on it.
White is as white as bubbles bubbling on top of the water, that feels
like silk.
White is as white as a polar bear in the North Pole jumping and
pouncing about.
White is as white as the road markings dividing the wide long road
as the cars go flying down it.
White is as white as an onion that makes you cry but is extremely
tasty to eat in spaghetti bolognaise.
White is as white as the thick icy snow waiting for a huge muddy
shoe to tread on it.
White is as white as icicles hanging from your roof, as the cold
water freezes.
White is as white as the inside of an apple.
White is as white as a bandage to heal a bleeding wound when you
hurt yourself badly.
White is as white as a parachute opening in the deep blue sky.

Rachel Huggins (9)
South Avenue Junior School

WHAT IS YELLOW?

What is yellow? The stars are yellow
Sparkling in the night sky.

What is yellow? A butterfly is yellow
Flitting in the clear blue sky.

What is yellow? A banana is yellow
Slipping, slopping out of its skin.

What is yellow? A topaz is yellow
Sparkling on a princess's beautiful hand.

What is yellow? The scorching sun is yellow
Glistening in the clear blue sky.

What is yellow? A sunflower is yellow
Opening its petals out to the sparkling sunlight.

What is yellow? The sand is yellow
Shimmering on a blazing beach.

Nakita Doyle (10)
South Avenue Junior School

SPACE ROCKET

The space rocket is getting ready to go,
Where it is going, I really don't know.
Spacemen are now going on board,
Fixing and fastening one last chord.
Off they blast, 3, 2, 1,
Up off into the blazing sun.
People wave and shout goodbye,
But the rocket flies off as quick as a sigh.

Bethan Blakely (10)
South Avenue Junior School

WHAT'S YELLOW?

What's yellow? A star is yellow,
twinkling, shining near the golden moon.

What's yellow? A moon is yellow, twinkling
in the golden sky coming up from noon.

What's yellow? Sand is yellow, small and
golden on the beach.

What's yellow? Eagles are yellow, and
they have a house captain to help you teach.

What's yellow? Lemons are yellow, they
are sweet and sour, they are lemons.

What's yellow? Melons are yellow, they are
round on the table, to be washed, they are melons.

Danielle Kemp (9)
South Avenue Junior School

WHAT IS BLUE?

What is blue?
The sky is blue, planes go through.
What is blue?
Blue Tack is blue, which sticks on to you.
What is blue?
Bluebells are blue, shaped like bells all the way through.
What is blue?
Ink is blue, smudging over my work.
What is blue?
The dark night is blue with stars shining bright at you.
What is blue?
Numeracy books are blue, we use them for maths.

Muslima Miah (9)
South Avenue Junior School

WHAT IS BLUE?

What is blue? The roaring ocean is blue
In the deep moonlight thro'.
What is blue? Chelsea is blue
And the players' T-shirts too.
What is blue? My pen's ink is blue
Running thro' my cartridge too.
What is blue? My funky starfish pencil case
Spare pencils and pens just in case.
What is blue? The lonely sky
There are lots of birds in the sky as they fly.
What is blue? The computer desk is blue
Isn't it lucky they don't have two.
What is blue? My working maths book
To make, make me look.
What is blue? Classic fiction is blue
All the way thro'.

Kylie Pierce (9)
South Avenue Junior School

THE SUN

The sun is as burning as a spit roast,
It's like a huge glowing fireball, shining in the sky,
It's as massive as the Empire State Building, tall and wide,
The sun is as yellow as a banana, ripe and fresh,
It's like a colossal sized torch, gleaming away,
The sun is as shiny as the stars,
Somewhere in the sky they are flashing away,
It's like a monster, with long, great big, huge arms,
It is a golden ball, rolling up and down each day.

Gary Chapman (10)
South Avenue Junior School

WHAT IS RED?

Red is a traffic light
That signals people to stop.

Red is Rudolph's nose
Glowing brightly in the sky at Christmas.

Red is your blood
Rushing through your veins.

Red is your heart
Pumping blood around your body.

Red is a plump tomato
Sitting at the back of a small fridge.

Red is a fox
Running in the park under the moonlit sky.

Red is a robin's breast
Being shown to other animals.

Red is tomato soup
Sitting in a dish by the microwave.

Red is molten lava
Slowly sliding down a bursting volcano.

Red is our handwriting pens
Writing on a plain piece of paper.

Red is a fire
Burning brightly in the dining room.

Red is a red pepper
Be careful, it is hot and spicy.

Charlotte Johnson (10)
South Avenue Junior School

WHAT IS RED?

Red is the sparkling lava sprouting
Out brightly from a volcano.

Red is your eyes flashing in
A funny photo of you!

Red is your face full of anger
Shining fiercely.

Red is your lips after you
Have eaten saucy tomato ketchup.

Red is a poppy swishing from
Side to side in a deserted field.

Red is a traffic light that means
Stop quickly!

Red is a warning sign beware
Danger ahead!

Red is a Christmas bauble
Flashing on a tree.

Red is the ruby sparkling
On a dainty lady's finger.

Red is the sun setting beautifully
Another day is over.

Danielle Holland (9)
South Avenue Junior School

WHAT IS ORANGE?

What is orange? Lava is orange
Pouring slowly out of a dark volcano.
Orange is a suntan developing
While relaxing on the beach for hours.
Orange is a tiger prowling fiercely
Through the creepy forest.
Orange is the sun setting
On a warm afternoon.
Orange is a juicy peach
Waiting to be eaten and enjoyed.
Orange is orangeade
With bubbles rising to the surface.
Orange is a bright light
Gleaming in the night.

Roxanne Butcher (9)
South Avenue Junior School

WHAT IS RED?

What is red?

Red is Liverpool's football kit
getting muddy.

Red is a bright red heart pumping rapidly
every second.

Red is Mars floating in the dark starry
midnight sky.

Red is a squirrel scampering up and down
a huge tree.

Lewis Jarrett (9)
South Avenue Junior School

WHAT IS THE COLOUR RED?

What is red? A ruby is red
Shining in the sunshine

What is red? A fox is red
Leaping through the long green grass

What is red? A rose is red
Glimmering with raindrops on Valentine's Day.

What is red? Lava is red
Bubbling with all its hot liquid.

What is red? A tomato is red
Oozing out as we eat it.

What is red? An old Arsenal shirt is red
Flying across the pitch on a hot windy day.

What is red? A traffic light is red
That means stop!

Rhiannon Burns (9)
South Avenue Junior School

RACING CAR

A racing car is a four-wheeled monster
roaring on the racetrack.

It is a missile,
crashing and never blowing up.

It is a dream car,
driving smoothly along.

James Cassidy (10)
South Avenue Junior School

WHAT IS RED?

What is red?
Red is a fire engine
Dashing at full speed to an emergency.

Red is a delicious scrumptious strawberry,
Ready to be munched by a greedy little girl.

> Red is a hungry fox
> Dashing as fast as lightning,
> Chasing after a little scared rabbit
>
> Red is a cunning devil,
> Coming up to earth,
> Looking for a lonely person to haunt

Red is delicious red wine
Splashing softly like a waterfall
Into a little glass

Red is heat
Spreading from the scorching, burning, hot sun,
To make the poor, sad people warm again.

Jamie Oswell (10)
South Avenue Junior School

THERE WAS A DOG

There was a dog called Cherry,
Who ate a poisonous berry,
He lived in Rome,
So he went home,
And lived the rest of his life very merry.

Kieran Thomsett (9)
South Avenue Junior School

BLUE

What is blue? A sapphire ring is blue
Sparkling in the glowing light.
What is blue? An exotic fish is blue
Darting in the coral reefs.
What is blue? A cold person is blue
Shivering in the deserted high street.
What is blue? Rain is blue
Falling softly through the night.
What is blue? Eyes are blue
Staring lovingly at you.
What is blue? Ink is blue
Flooding out of a leaky pen.
What is blue? A sweet blueberry is blue
Waiting to be eaten on a plastic plate.
What is blue? The sky is blue
On a lovely sunny day.
What is blue? A ball of wool is blue
Being played with by a naughty kitten.
What is blue? Why blue is just blue!

Beth Hawkins (10)
South Avenue Junior School

LOVE

Love is pink.
It is a flame on a candle, at a romantic dinner.
It is strawberries and cream.
Love is waking up in your comfy bed.
It is Vivaldi's Four Seasons.
It is a blood-red rose shimmering in the sun.

Rebecca Calver (10)
South Avenue Junior School

WHAT IS RED?

What is red?
Red is a ruby sparkling in the sunlight

> Red is blood
> Rushing through our veins

Red is a fox,
Jumping for his prey

> Anger is red,
> Lashing out at you.

What is red?
Arsenal's football shorts
Getting muddy on the slippery soggy grass

> Red is the Hogwarts Express
> Blazing sparks down the rusty train track

Red is?
Fire blazing higher every second

> Red is?
> A lobster pinching people every second it's got.

Kyle Davy Simmers (10)
South Avenue Junior School

THE YOUNG LADY

There was a young lady who loved to cook toast.
But she had never attempted to cook a Sunday roast.
She fried the swede, and roasted the peas.
Eventually, she ended up having toast instead of a roast.

Beth Shrubsall (10)
South Avenue Junior School

WHAT IS RED?

What is red?
Red is a poppy swaying in an enormous storm.

> Red is a fox
> Hunting for its prey.

Lips are red
Waiting to kiss a lucky someone.

> What is red?
> A fire engine zooming to a fire.

Red is a berry
Dangling from a piece of holly.

> Anger is red
> Lashing out at someone.

What is red?
A ruby sparkling in the sunlight.

> Red is blood
> Streaming out of a stinging cut.

Liam O'Donoghue (10)
South Avenue Junior School

THE SUN IS . . .

The sun is a juicy orange waiting to be eaten.
The sun is a fierce lion with a mane like a line of swords.
The sun is an ancient Egyptian treasure sparkling in the sky.
The sun is a bright yellow flower dying as the day goes on.
The sun is an orange Frisbee flying through the air.
The sun is a red cricket ball zooming at the stumps.

James Turnbull (10)
South Avenue Junior School

WHAT IS BLUE?

What is blue?
Blue is a blue tit gliding thro' the calm air.

Blue is sadness
When gently tears drip down your upset face

Blue is a bluebell
Swishing in the sun.

Blue is the sea
Gently lapping on a sandy, scalding beach

Blue is cold
When your soft cheeks gleam red

Blue tastes like blueberries
When all the scrumptious juice squirts out.

Blue is the sky
With all the thick, fluffy clouds floating by.

Tasnima Sultana (10)
South Avenue Junior School

LONELINESS

Loneliness is a dark sort of white,
Painted on the walls of an empty room.
It tastes like a dirty marshmallow,
With the forever-lasting memory in your mouth.
Loneliness sounds like a long line of an echoing voice.
It feels like a cold breeze
Hitting you by surprise.
Loneliness smells like a gust of smoke,
Floating through the air.

Lia Lindsay (10)
South Avenue Junior School

WHAT IS SILVER?

What is silver? Silver is the stars
Shimmering in the moonlight.
Silver is the touch of spiky icicles
When bitter ice hits your fingertips.
Silver is the sight of a glimmer
Diamond in the darkness.
Silver is a dolphin that swims
Blissfully through the calm gentle sea.
Silver is the sour taste of spite.
Silver is bravery bright and bold.
Silver is the winter when the cold ice gleams.
Silver is a choir singing contentedly.
Silver is a silver medal near the top
                but not quite.

Alicia Sheppard (10)
South Avenue Junior School

THE STARS

The stars are diamonds upon a velvet cushion
Glimmering in the moonlight.
They are the glint of a dragon's eye.
Flying through the dark blue sky.
They are the graceful azure eyes of a cat,
looking modest and tenderly about the world it lives in.
They are nibs of fountain pens,
Smoothly rolling on top of paper.
They are the frightful flames
Of a spitting fire growing larger and *larger.*
They are the gorgeous shine of teeth,
Pure white, coming out of the dentist.

Laura Randall (11)
South Avenue Junior School

WHAT IS GREEN?

What is green? A forest is green,
with leaves that cover the angry bears that are always
ready to jump out at you, so beware of bears.

An apple is green,
nice and ready to be eaten.

A crocodile is green,
with big sharp teeth ready to eat you.

A meadow is green,
with deer charging at you ready to fight.

A garden is green,
with grass and flowers and little fir trees growing huge.

Summer is green,
it has nice soft grass and flowers.

Lewis Hance (9)
South Avenue Junior School

MY HOMOPHONE POEM

I went to see the sea
But I could not see the sea so

I went to ask Mo if she could mow the lawn
But I could not find Mo to mow the lawn so

I went to Wales to find some whales
But I could not find any whales so

After that I just went home.

Kimberley Cato (10)
South Avenue Junior School

WHAT IS THE SUN?

The sun is a juicy satsuma,
waiting to be eaten.

It is a yellow beach ball
being thrown high into the sky.

It is a golden ring,
on a rich lady's finger.

It is a rubber dinghy,
sailing across the calm sea.

It is a light,
directing sailors to land.

The sun is a candle,
waiting for darkness.

Sally Barnes (11)
South Avenue Junior School

NIGHTMARE

A Nightmare, her hooves drumming in my head.
Nostrils flaring, and her eyes burning like fire.
Mane and tail flowing, she's a black devil.
Rearing and bucking, kicking and plunging.
Biting, she's full of vice, she'll never be caught.
She's born to be free.
She's nothing like her cousin the Dream.
Nightmare,
The fastest horse in the galaxy.

Leanne Downs (11)
South Avenue Junior School

DEEP BLUE SEA

A shark is the Devil, complete with gleaming, razor-sharp teeth.
This uncanny predator is a ravenous, bloodthirsty beast
intent on devouring anything.
A shark is a mindless eating machine.
A colossal, consuming corrupter with a mammoth-sized mouth,
it's a teeming pit full of snakes, scarabs and scorpions.
Each one a ferocious flesh-eater.
With lifeless black eyes, it's a phantom of the ocean,
But as soon as it bites those eyes roll over with pure pleasure.

Deep Blue Sea.

Ryan Burns (11)
South Avenue Junior School

THE BATH

The bubbles in my bath
are like the fluffy clouds
on a warm summer's day.

The rain is like the hot running tap.

Hailstones are like
smelly bombs you drop in your bath.

The rough waves are like someone scrubbing
down my back.

The wind is like someone emerging from
a warm bath.

Rebecca Baldock (11)
South Avenue Junior School

WHAT IS THE SUN?

The sun is a light bulb,
far away in the bright sky.

The sun is an orange beach ball,
thrown up into the air.

The sun is a white chocolate button,
dropped on my sizzling tongue.

The sun is an oval pebble,
washed up on to a sandy seashore.

The sun is a golden ring,
on a lady's sleek finger.

The sun is the letter 'a',
sitting on a blank line.

The sun is a baked bean,
in a blue bowl.

The sun is a jellyfish,
swimming around under the clear water.

The sun is . . .

Hayley Kent (11)
South Avenue Junior School

THE ICICLE

An icicle is a gleaming crystal,
Reaching for the snowy ground,
Sparkling in the light,
An icicle is a great glistening masterpiece.

James Harding (10)
South Avenue Junior School

CAT COUNTDOWN

Ten cats sitting on the wall
one went to dine
then there were nine

Nine cats sitting on the wall
one saw his mate
then there were eight

Eight cats sitting on the wall
one went to Devon
then there were seven

Seven cats sitting on the wall
One got tics
then there were six

Six cats sitting on the wall
one fell in a hive
then there were five

Five cats sitting on the wall
one broke the law
then there were four

Four cats sitting on the wall
one saw me
then there were three

Three cats sitting on the wall
one saw you
then there were two

Two cats sitting on the wall
one weighed a ton
then there was one

One cat sitting on the wall
he wasn't having fun
then there were none.

Kaylie Peartree (10)
South Avenue Junior School

HAPPINESS

Happiness is pink
like a comfy blow-up chair

It is the smell of melting marshmallow
cooking on a summer's eve

Happiness sounds like the wind
settling on the fresh green grass

It is the feel of silk
running over a baby face

Happiness tastes like Rice Krispies
crackling on your tongue

It looks like red roses,
growing with every drop of the rain

Happiness makes me want to play
and never, ever stop.

Vikki Headon (11)
South Avenue Junior School

TEN WRIGGLING WORMS

Ten wriggly worms
sliding up the path
One landed on a mine
then there were nine.

Nine wriggly worms
sliding up the path
One had to decide his fate
then there were eight.

Eight wriggly worms
sliding up the path
One took a short cut to Devon
then there were seven.

Seven wriggly worms
sliding up the path
One went on SMTV Live
then there were five.

Five wriggly worms
sliding up the path
One slipped underneath a door
then there were four.

Four wriggly worms
sliding up the path
One got called for tea
then there were three.

Three wriggly worms
sliding up the path
One shouted out 'Moo'
then there were two.

Two wriggly worms
sliding up the path
One got squashed by a thumb
then there was one.

One wriggly worm
sliding up the path
He became a superhero
then there were zero.

Michael Baxendale (10)
South Avenue Junior School

WHAT IS . . . AN ORANGE?

An orange is an
orange spotty face waiting
to be opened to the sunlight.

It is a football
waiting to score.

It is a glass of
orangeade spitting
Vitamin C

It is an orange
hand flicking pips
right in your eye.

It is a goldfish
swimming in a fruit bowl.

It is fire making
me hot and orange.

John Jones (10)
South Avenue Junior School

SADNESS

Sadness is grey
It tastes like cauliflower.
Bland and tasteless on my tongue.
It sounds like crying.
Sobbing all night long.
It feels like sticky mud,
Clinging to my wellington boots,
Heavy, dragging me down.
It smells like burning rubber,
Choking me.

Aaron Blackbourn (10)
South Avenue Junior School

KYLE

There was a young lad called Kyle
Who had to sort out his file
It took him all day
To sort out his hay
And then he had a neat pile.

Kyle Clarke (11)
South Avenue Junior School

FIVE SENSES OF A SNOWMAN

Its colour is white.
It tastes like strawberries.
It sounds like Christmas morning.
It feels like a frozen man.
It smells like a white Christmas.

John Gibson (11)
South Avenue Junior School

THE SPIDER

I walk along the window sill and look to my right, what do I see?
I see people examining me and children look and then run away.
I don't want to hurt anyone, I just want to have some friends
But that's impossible,
I mean, look at me!
I have eight legs and a hairy body and my eyes don't get me started!
The other bugs point and laugh (apart from the other spiders like me)
Whenever I spin a web, it breaks because a child kicks a football
                                                          through it
And now I am homeless and on this window sill.

Afrin Shohid (10)
South Avenue Junior School

HORSES

When you ride, the horse will stride,
jump, gallop and walk.

When you move it feels really smooth,
When you jump you land with a bump.

Horses wear tack when they go
on a hack.

Fay, Jack, Nessie, Jasper and Troy
are bay,
And Barney, Breeze, Bonny, Bobby and
Rosie like eating hay.

Emily Robinson (8)
Teynham CE Primary School

A SPRING DAY

It's spring today
Winter's gone away
The sun is so light
Flowers and leaves so bright
People sunbathing and playing on beaches
Trees growing apples, pears and peaches
Go out to parks, have a lot of fun
Go for tea, crisps and maybe a bun
So hot, so dry
But I'm still glad winter's gone by
Don't need no cover, or no quilt
I feel like a wet building
Just built.
But now it's time to go to sleep
Now everyone's resting,
Not one little peep.

Hannah Sears (8)
Teynham CE Primary School

THE DEEP BLUE SEA

While I was swimming under the sea
What wonderful creatures I did see
While I was swimming under the deep blue sea
The dolphins came up and swam with me
What a joy it was for me to see,
All the dolphins in the sea,
Swimming along happily with me,
In the tranquillity of
The
Deep blue sea.

Jack Bigwood (8)
Teynham CE Primary School

SPRING

Spring, spring is the best
When the leaves grow again
Spring, spring is such fun
To see the lambs come out with Mum.
Daffodils growing in the sun
With lots of people having fun.
Birds out singing while
Foxes hunting.
Loads of blossom on the trees
With buzzing bees getting
                    their precious pollen.

Pasie Thompson (10)
Teynham CE Primary School

A LITTLE BROWN MOUSE

I am looking for a house
Said a little brown mouse

One for my brother
One for me
One for my sister
That makes three.

One to dance in when I have a ball
A dining room, a bedroom
Six in all.

James Robinson (10)
Teynham CE Primary School

THE LITTLE, OLD, FAT MAN

There once was a man
A little man
A little, old, fat man
Who got stuck in a pan
A frying pan
A big frying pan
He called for his cat
His black cat
His black and white cat
But the man
The little man
The little, old, fat man
Was just too fat
So he ended up living there.

Sean Elsey (9)
Teynham CE Primary School

SNAKES

I saw a snake
and his name was Jake.
One day in the lake
he met a mate.
Her name was Kate.
They went out one
day to the lake
and how the sun
did bake.

Jamie Underdown (9)
Teynham CE Primary School

CATS

I have a cat
Which for it I care
His coat is plain grey
For a cat, it's rare.

His name is Smokey
Cos he's the colour of smoke
I like all different colours
My mom likes gingery yolk
My brother's got a cat
Who is all white and tabby
My brother's name's Tyler and the cat's called Tom
And he hates the sight of a dog.

Kristy Alethea Adams (9)
Teynham CE Primary School

CATS

Cats are nice and fluffy
Like bats, hats, rats.
Bikes are fast and so are cats
Cats are warm and so are hats.
Rats are clever and so are cats.
Cats sometimes have owners
Who give them food and drink.
They pounce to catch their prey
Like rats and snakes.
They're very nice and kind.

Kevin Yates (10)
Teynham CE Primary School

MOUSE

I got a fright the other night,
Whilst looking out my house.
Over the fence and across the lawn
There ran a little mouse.
He hopped up on the garden shed
And came through my trees
And tapped upon the window sill
And asked me for some cheese.

Charlotte Hogg (9)
Teynham CE Primary School

BOYSIE

Boysie is big and brown.
He has a spiky coat.
He runs fast as he chases the ball.
He comes towards me when I call him.
He has his own special chair
Which he covers with his spiky hair
And he loves me very dearly.

Nathan Auckland
Teynham CE Primary School

MY DOG BERTIE

I love my dog Bertie
Though he gets dirty,
I don't care about the floor
Or his dirty paw.

I like it when he jumps
And chews Dad's pumps
My dog is called Bertie
I wish I had thirty.

Rebekah Harris (8)
Teynham CE Primary School

A PERFECT STORM

There was a bear who had a boat
And on the way he found a note.
It said there was going to be a storm,
A perfect storm

   Ahhhhhh . . .

He heard a thud and saw a source
      of blood.

Joe Gregory (10)
Teynham CE Primary School

SPRING

Winds blowing, trees flowing.
Birds flying, sun's rising.
Cats roaring, rabbits snoring
    in their burrows.
Eggs cracking, chicks bursting.
Grass growing, Dad's mowing.
It will soon be summer again.

James Joseph Bures (9)
Teynham CE Primary School

THE TREE

I looked out of my window and saw a tree.
It was standing all alone staring at me.

How it stands all so sad.
All alone, oh how bad.

Its leaves rustle in the wind.
I feel so sorry for it.

People walk by wearing scarves
The tree's brown conkers fall on paths.

People walk past not noticing the tree,
But I know deep down inside
                    it's something special.

Charlotte Bones (10)
Teynham CE Primary School

HALLOWE'EN

On a cold and autumn morning,
Hallowe'en is not boring.
We have costumes, who's the best?
There's the wicked witch of the west.

Ghosts and ghoulies come out to play,
The witches and wizards do everything their way.
Hallowe'en is almost over,
And Dad will take me home in his Rover.

Alicia Murton (10)
Teynham CE Primary School

SPIDERS

They creep, they crawl, they sit on your wall.
They crawl down the pipe,
And eat things that are ripe.
They have hair, they have flare,
You can hold them if you dare!

Emma Taylor (10)
Teynham CE Primary School

CATS

Do bats eat cats or cats eat bats?
Do rats eat cats or cats eat rats?
Do cats sit on mats or mats sit on cats?
Do cats wear hats or hats wear cats?

Jamie Showell (10)
Teynham CE Primary School

CATS

Cats don't like bats
Bats don't like cats
Cats lie on mats
Bats hang on trees.

Danica Parsons (10)
Teynham CE Primary School